Portland Community College

WITHDRAWN

The Portland Bridge Book

The Portland Bridge Book

Third Edition

Text by

Sharon Wood Wortman with Ed Wortman

Photographs by

James Norman

Drawings by

Joseph Boquiren

with a Foreword by

Eric DeLony

Edited by

Ed Wortman and Charlie White

Urban Adventure Press

This book was supported in part by generous grants from David Evans & Associates Engineering, OBEC Consulting Engineers, and contractors Abhe & Svoboda.

Urban Adventure Press
PO Box 3403
Portland OR 97208-3403
© 2006 by Urban Adventure Press
All rights reserved. Published 2006.

First Edition, 1989. Second Edition 2001. Third Edition 2006.
Printed in the United States of America

ISBN: 0-9787365-0-8 (Hardcover)
ISBN: 0-9787365-1-6 (Softcover)

Library of Congress Preassigned Control Number Data

Wood Wortman, Sharon, 1944—
    The Portland Bridge Book / text by Sharon Wood Wortman with Ed Wortman
    Foreword by Eric DeLony, photos by James Norman, drawings by Joseph Boquiren.—
    Third ed.
    Includes bibliographical references and index.
    1. Bridges-Oregon-Portland. I. Title   2006935152

The paper used in this publication meets the minimum requirements of the American National Standard for Information Sciences—Permanence of Paper for Printed Library Materials, ANSI Z39.48-1984.

Cover photo: Fremont Bridge at Willamette River mile 11.1 in Portland, Oregon by James Norman for the Historic American Engineering Record/Oregon Department of Transportation, 1999

Frontispiece: Aerial photo of the bridges of Portland ca. 1940, courtesy Mark Falby

ROUGH STEEL

A bridge is like a relationship.
You work hard and for a long time
to make it strong and then you can expect
nothing to change, so when
the relationship has to carry
an unexpected heavy load,
it bounces right back
to where it was before.

Amira Shagaga
Leanna Garrison's sixth grade class
Taft Middle School, Lincoln City, Oregon
2004

CONTENTS

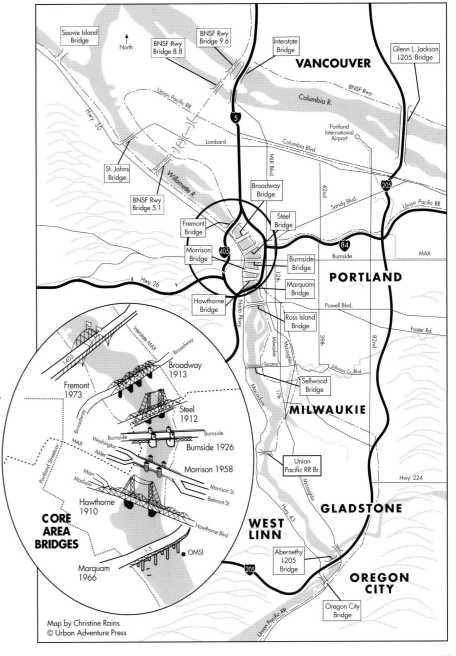

Appendices

Historic American Engineering Record/Oregon Department of Transportation
"Willamette River Bridges Recording Project, 1999"

Movable Bridge Drawings, by Joseph Boquiren

FOREWORD

by Eric DeLony

Looking north from the Hawthorne Bridge, 1905 Morrison in foreground.

PORTLAND IS ONE OF THE WORLD'S GREAT BRIDGE CITIES where the urban core is defined by one or more rivers crossed by bridges. Paris, London, Pittsburgh, Cleveland, New York, Chicago, and Los Angeles are others. Like many of these cities, Portland is growing to understand that bridges, in addition to their functional value, can serve as powerful architectural monuments giving identity and character to a city. Ten such highway bridges exist within a 16-mile stretch of the Lower Willamette River, with an eleventh now being constructed to Sauvie Island across the Willamette River's Multnomah Channel. Of these, five are significant features of one-mile-long Governor Tom McCall Waterfront Park, one of Portland's finest urban achievements and the grassy platform for a dozen annual downtown festivals and celebrations.

Before Portland's bridges could become distinctive urban attributes, however, the riverfront and the bridges had to be accessible to pedestrians and bicyclists. In 1973, with the opening of the Fremont Bridge, six-lane Harbor Drive was replaced with Tom McCall Waterfront Park.

Extending 22 blocks along the west bank of the Willamette River, the park was dedicated in 1978. This single act gained instant fame for the Rose City. Portland became one of the first American cities to reclaim its waterfront. The park not only returned access to the river to its citizens, but also sparked further urban redevelopment. Through this process, continuing with the opening of the $31 million Vera Katz Eastbank Esplanade in 2001, Portland has become a textbook city for urban revitalization and has earned the distinction of being one of America's first and foremost "livable" cities. It has the potential of becoming a world-class bridge city comparable to London or Paris. Anyone who has visited these European capitals cannot help but be impressed by the bridges along the Seine's quays in Paris or the Thames's embankments in London. In Paris, 36 bridges, most arches, connect the Left Bank to the Right Bank. In Greater London, Tower Bridge and 32 others cross the Thames. Occasionally there is the need for a new construction, but generally the decision has been to restore and rehabilitate these historic spans for another century.

In addition to Portland, other American cities are following the European precedent. New York has invested millions refurbishing the Brooklyn, Manhattan, Williamsburg, Queensboro, and other East River bridges. Pittsburgh has restored Gustav Lindenthal's magnificent lenticular trusses on the Smithfield Street Bridge. Other spans on the Monongahela and Allegheny have been carefully rehabilitated and the city has spent millions refurbishing the "Point," an urban park in the heart of former Steel City. Cleveland, as part of its sesquicentennial, spent $4.9 million lighting the viaducts and bridges crossing "The Flats," another reclaimed industrial area along the banks of the Cuyahoga River. Following the Loma Prieta earthquake in 1989, Los Angeles spent millions seismically retrofitting former L.A. City Engineer Merrill Butler's ten City Beautiful bridges over the Los Angeles River. Chicago has done likewise, rehabilitating its bascules over the Chicago River, including lighting the bridges and river walls at night.

It takes effort to establish and maintain a thriving city. Portland is an example of what happens when citizens take risks—it was one of the first U.S. cities to reclaim its waterfront and one of the first to put human beings ahead of automobiles. It did this by building the Metropolitan Area Express (MAX) light rail as the linchpin of the city's multimodal transport system. Now, the Portland Streetcar also offers free transit in the downtown area, with more plans afoot for expanding public transit.

Tom McCall Waterfront Park has been extended to the other side of the river via the mile-long Esplanade. With a pedestrian and bicycle RiverWalk pathway cantilevered from the lower deck of the Steel Bridge and the enlarged pedestrian and bicycle walkways on the recently restored Hawthorne, it is possible to bike or hike a five-mile circuit on both sides of the river. The new River District residential area north of the Steel Bridge brings more people to this part of the extended waterfront where Multnomah County is carrying out a $40 million, multi-year rehabilitation of the Broadway Bridge. The same can be found toward the south where Tom McCall Waterfront Park has been extended from the Hawthorne to the Marquam Bridge. This area includes a beach for swimming.

Despite its recreational value, the lower Willamette always has been a working river with a constant flow of vessels ranging from high-masted schooners in the 19th century to deep-draft grain ships and all manner of tugs, barges, and pleasure craft. Unless the bridges are modern high-level structures like the St. Johns suspension span or the Fremont arch, the bridges must be able to get out of the way. Movable bridges are the distinction of Portland's bridge collection. The first movable on the Willamette was the Morrison, a swing span completed in 1887. However, the center piers for swing spans were obstacles to navigation so eventually they were replaced by bascules and vertical lifts that make way for larger ships. Movable bridges come in three forms and Portland has examples of all three: bascule (Broadway, Burnside, Morrison), vertical lift (Steel, Hawthorne, Interstate, BNSF Railway 5.1), and swing (BNSF 8.8 and 9.6). In addition, Portland is home to the other main bridge types: arch (2008 Sauvie Island, Fremont, Oregon City), beam or truss (Marquam, Ross Island, Sellwood, Abernethy, Glenn L. Jackson, Union Pacific Railroad Bridge at Lake Oswego), and suspension (St. Johns). These are the bridges featured in *The Portland Bridge Book*.

Ms. Wood Wortman's passion for bridges started when she sold the idea to *The Oregonian* newspaper to write a series about the city's bridges in 1984. These 11 articles evolved into the first edition of this book. Since then, she has been part of the wave of bridge scholarship and interest that has grown throughout the United States over the last thirty years. Driving this interest is the fact that many of America's bridges are aging and wearing out. Some are scheduled for replacement. To address the question of which bridges might be historic and worthy of preservation, many states have inventoried their historic spans. In 1995, Dwight

The Interstate Bridge as viewed from Oregon looking north.

Smith, James Norman, and Pieter Dykman of the Oregon Department of Transportation (ODOT) published the results of their historic bridge survey in *Historic Highway Bridges of Oregon*. The remarkable diversity, beauty, engineering ingenuity, and historical significance of Oregon's bridges were revealed for the first time.

I traveled to this great Northwestern state soon thereafter to see them. Dwight Smith and I spent several glorious days touring Oregon's coastal Route 101, photographing former State Bridge Engineer Conde McCullough's coastal spans. We negotiated a HAER (Historic American Engineering Record) recording

project to document a selection of these spans and Oregon's other historic bridges during the summer of 1990. It was during one of these trips that I got to meet Sharon Wood, Portland's Bridge Lady.

Oregon has been very good to HAER. In 1994 and 1995, HAER and ODOT recorded projects along the Columbia River Gorge Scenic Highway. In the summer of 1999, a team of six architects, two full-time historians, a half-time historian, and photographer James Norman documented ten of the Willamette River bridges. Sharon was one of the full-time historians on the team and Ed Wortman served as the project's engineering advisor.

The second edition of *The Portland Bridge Book*, published in 2001, benefited from that work.

In recognition of ODOT's stewardship of historic bridges over the last two decades, not only in Portland but also throughout the state, the National Trust for Historic Preservation presented the agency with a National Preservation Honor Award for its Historic Bridge Preservation Program in 2005.

For history buffs, the designers of Portland's bridges read like a who's who of early 20th century engineering: Gustav Lindenthal, John Alexander Low Waddell, David B. Steinman, Ralph Modjeski, Joseph B. Strauss, Conde B. McCullough, and Ira Hedrick. During 1922 and 1923, Othmar Ammann, who would go on to design the George Washington, Bayonne, Triborough, Bronx-Whitestone, Throgs Neck, and Verrazano-Narrows bridges in New York City, helped with the calculations of Portland's Ross Island, Sellwood, and Burnside bridges for Lindenthal in Lindenthal's New York City office. Lindenthal, himself a titan of early American engineering, designed New York's Queensboro Bridge and the Hell Gate Arch. I remember wondering why Portland had access to such outstanding bridge engineers. Certainly, in the early 20th century, there was ample bridge talent on the West Coast. Our conclusion was that nearly all the city's bridges, particularly the big movables, were specialty bridges requiring the expertise of engineers skilled not only in the civil engineering of bridge design, but also in mechanical engineering, since many of the bridges moved.

The text of the third edition updates each bridge's most recent physical changes (rehabilitations and implementation of computerized opening technology among the many), and adds a chapter on the Sauvie Island Bridge. The visual effects in the third edition are striking. This is a much more visual book, with attention to layout, page typography, overall design, and detail, due, in part, to the addition of the HAER photographs and drawings. Featured are the photographs of James Norman who not only is the manager of the Oregon Department of Transportation Environmental Planning Unit and a co-author of *Historic Highway Bridges of Oregon*, but also was the HAER photographer for the 1999 Willamette River Bridge Recording Project. The third edition includes lovely historic photographic views of the earlier bridges providing depth and allowing the reader to go back in time to compare what exists today with that of yesterday, and also to see what the bridges looked like during construction. It also features the drawings of Joseph Boquiren, one of six architects on the HAER team who drew measured drawings of Portland's bridges for the 1999 study.

For these reasons and more, *The Portland Bridge Book* works as an engineering reference, a history book, or just an enjoyable story. Anyone who enjoys bridges, rivers, history, storytelling, music, poetry, or Portland will find these pages entertaining and full of information.

All in all, it is not only a remarkable work of bridge scholarship and writing, and not only a gift to the citizens and visitors to one of the world's foremost bridge cities, but also a model for other American locations with collections of historic bridges. I hope that the leadership of Portland will be inspired by this book to continue their quest for excellence in improving the image and livability of their remarkable city. For example, I would like to see all the Central City bridges illuminated, as is common practice in European cities. The Willamette Light Brigade, a citizens group, has been working since 1987—almost twenty years—to illuminate Portland's bridges. Architectural lighting adds another dimension to a bridge's symbolic presence and majesty. Imagine the towers of St. Johns and Steel, or the undersides of the bascules at Broadway and Burnside illuminated. This would add immeasurably to the nocturnal image of the city and the memory one takes away.

I would also like to see wayside markers interpreting the amazing legacy of Portland's bridges. Having gone to the trouble and expense to rehabilitate all these structures, it only seems logical to explain why and how this was done.

To learn more about Portland's bridges, you need to read *The Portland Bridge Book*, or get to know the bridges personally by joining Sharon Wood Wortman on one of her walks.

Eric DeLony
Chief (Retired), Historic American Engineering Record
National Park Service

PREFACE TO THE THIRD EDITION

St. Johns Bridge east end anchorage.

IF THE FIRST EDITION OF *THE PORTLAND BRIDGE BOOK*, published in 1989 when I was a single woman, was a single-span bridge and the second edition, published in 2001, after I met bridge engineer Ed Wortman, was an arch, then this third edition, published nine years after our marriage, is surely a suspension bridge. Suspension bridges—expensive technology reserved for crossing wide bodies of water or canyons—are rare in Oregon. Two tall towers and twin cables anchored to the earth and reinforced concrete hold up deck, traffic, and weather. I think of Ed, who has been climbing around big highway bridges for more than 40 years, like the anchorage chain buried in basalt on the west side of the St. Johns Bridge, the only major highway suspension bridge in the Willamette Valley. His contribution is largely out of sight, while I am the 29,000-ton anchorage sitting in Cathedral Park on the bridge's east end. The fact is I would be little more than hollow concrete without Ed on the other side of the river supporting the fight against gravity that's been required for this book's updated content and continued publication.

Like the rehabilitation of bridges, updating and revising The *Portland Bridge Book* has been a consuming, ongoing, and necessary process. People ask "Why more than one edition? Doesn't one sufficiently told tale take care of history?" The thing is, history keeps moving. It's been 17 years since the first edition, five years since the second, and now a third edition in 2006 reflects the acceleration of events in the bridge world. Bridge design and construction technology are rapidly changing. For example, with a 4,624-foot main span, the Humber Bridge in England held the record for the world's longest suspension bridge until 1981. Three bridges have out-distanced it since; the latest, the Akashi-Kaiyko Bridge in Japan, opened in 1998 with a main span of almost 6,000 feet, and in 2006 a contract was signed to build a $3.4 billion suspension bridge with a 10,000-foot main span across Messina Straits between mainland Italy and Sicily! By comparison, St. Johns' main span is 1,200 feet and the Golden Gate's main span is 4,200 feet.

Portland's aging bridges are constantly undergoing upgrades and rehabilitation to mechanical and structural systems. Three of the five Portland-core Willamette River bridges are more than 90 years old. A fourth is 80 this year, with the fifth turning 50 in 2008. Since the 2001 edition, there has been considerable increase in federal and Oregon Transportation Investment Act funding, granting several bridges a reprieve. The Oregon Department of Transportation finished a $43 million rehabilitation of the St. Johns Bridge in 2006, replacing its highway deck, sidewalks, street lighting, and paint. As part of Broadway's ongoing $40 million makeover, its mechanical parts were repaired and it was given new paint, street lighting, sidewalks, and lift span deck. Broadway's dangerous and worn-smooth open grating has now been replaced with fiber reinforced polymer—the first major bascule bridge in the country equipped with space-age material. Upstream, the Burnside Bridge is in the middle of a two-year lift span rehabilitation project scheduled to finish by the end of 2007. Burnside's $9 million contract calls for the concrete on its lift span deck to be removed and replaced, with replacement of large mechanical parts that open the bridge. In 1999, another Multnomah County bridge, the 1910 Hawthorne, the oldest operating vertical lift bridge in the U.S., was repaired, repainted, and upgraded at a cost of $21.5 million. And if you notice a difference in Hawthorne's two 900,000-pound counterweights, the Willamette Light Brigade (see Bridge Glossary) repainted both crimson in 2006 to better reflect Hawthorne's latest architectural lighting system—also new since the second edition.

When visiting third-grade classrooms I say, "Listen up, you little taxpayers." The challenge is how do we pay for taking care of this historically unique infrastructure so expensive to maintain? Most of Portland's bridges are eligible for or listed in the National Register of Historic Places and there is now a move afoot to nominate them as a group as Civil Engineering Landmarks. In a country of 600,000 highway bridges, our bridges are definitely aging, my point in this poem:

BRIDGES THAT OPEN LIKE OYSTERS

It is more than sand that gravels.
People always asking,
How long will that bridge last?
Broadway, Burnside,
and Morrison: all three bascules
bridging the twentieth
century, all three beneficiaries
of countless redos:
debrided surfaces, new
stainless steel bearing joints
and now tiny wires implanted
to track stress and strain.
Protected from silt and too much salt
and attended by at least one
good tender, no telling
how long succulence
will remain succulent,
or when an oyster will gulp for air,
opening, opening, opening
for the last time—
tight muscles no longer stopping traffic.

In these third graders' lifetimes, usage will increase exponentially. According to the 2000 U.S. census, from 1990 to 2000, Oregon's population increased by 20.4%, with an 8.9% growth in Portland. In 2006, more than a million vehicles a day, plus bicyclists and pedestrians, use the Portland-area bridges—*per day*. Demand has never been greater with ever-expanding projected population and crossing counts. Two bridges where demand has exceeded supply are the Sellwood and Interstate bridges. Since the publication of the second edition, citizen task forces have been formed to study and propose solutions for each of these crossings. In another case of overuse, the 1950 Sauvie Island Bridge has worn out and is now being replaced by a new arch bridge opening in 2008. The history of the old bridge and a description of the construction of the new bridge—the first new river bridge built by Multnomah County in 50 years—are included in this third edition.

This version also has a foreword. Eric DeLony, author of *Landmark American Bridges* (American Society of Civil Engineers, 1992), is the former chief of the Historic American Engineering Record and was in charge of the HAER/National Park Service 1999 study and documentation of the lower Willamette River bridges for the Library of Congress. Eric's foreword compares Portland's bridges to bridges all over the world.

The Bridge Glossary has been revised and expanded. Thanks to Ed Wortman's background and patience, we now have 198 engineering terms, up from 168 in the second edition. Notice, too, the subtitle "Technical Terms in Ordinary Language." We labored to create bridge engineering language easy on the syllables for both third graders and their

teachers. Included, too, are the major pedestrian bridges opened in 2006 on the Springwater Trail Corridor and the Portland Tramway, the city's first aerial bridge, opening in late 2006, if the gondolas go according to schedule.

Ed also contributed the chapter How and Why Bridges Are Built—subjects explored here using the Sauvie Island Bridge as example and reference.

Perhaps the most visual change is the book's artwork and format. This edition comes with architectural drawings and historic and contemporary photographs. James Norman, the photographer, was the photographer for the 1999 HAER study and is the co-author of *Historic Highway Bridges of Oregon* and other books. Joseph Boquiren, a Portland-based artist and architect, was one of six architects and field foreman for the HAER project's architectural drawings. Mark Falby, an independent book designer, worked with James to create the book's format and feel, shortening page width so *The Portland Bridge Book* will fit better on a shelf.

Last, the book has a new publisher. The Oregon Historical Society published the first and second editions, for which I am eternally grateful. This great and important publishing house ceased publishing all but its *Oregon Historical Society Quarterly* in July 2006, with the University of Washington continuing as distributor for 16 OHS Press titles. Therefore, Urban Adventure Press, an imprint I founded in 2005, is publishing this edition, continuing the work OHS began 17 years ago. To date, Urban Adventure Press has published four other titles. These include a 50-page guide for making models of the Willamette River bridges

using wooden craft sticks and truss patterns. In addition to *Bridge in a Box* and two poetry chapbooks, Urban Adventure Press has also produced *Connections—A Guide to Walking Portland's Central City Bridges*. A companion to *The Portland Bridge Book*, this large format brochure contains thumbnail photographs and concise descriptions of Fremont, Broadway, Steel, Burnside, Morrison, Hawthorne, Marquam, and Ross Island bridges, with colored map and step-by-step walking directions from Old Town to the Broadway Bridge to the Hawthorne Bridge, as well as driving directions to the St. Johns Bridge. *Walking Portland's Bridges Using Poetry as a Compass* is due out in late 2007. This literary guidebook features the poetry and lyrics of Northwest poets and songwriters who have read and performed during my bridge walks for the public sponsored by Portland Parks & Outdoor Recreation.

In a poetry and music service at the First Unitarian Church in Portland in July 2006, Lawson Inada said he doubted a person could be spiritually connected if he or she couldn't find a place to know and call home. In the end, any edition of *The Portland Bridge Book* is about clarifying this place where bridges keep the structures of our lives enormously and profusely together—the downtown part of our home connected about every one-third mile and, so far, steady and dry. *Poco en poco vamos lejos*— little by little we get far. May this edition anchor the reader's understanding and appreciation for even a short stretch along the river of history.

Sharon Wood Wortman
October 26, 2006

Note: The first preface of *The Portland Bridge Book* describes how Derek Ranta's fifth grade report formed the foundation for my initial research for a series about the bridges published by *The Oregonian* in 1984. The preface from the second edition describes where bridges took me professionally and personally, including that first date with Ed Wortman to a 13-foot-tall bearing of the Fremont Bridge at the exact spot where 7,500 tons, one-quarter of Fremont's weight, pushes into the ground. For the complete text of the first and second edition prefaces, go to <www.bridgestories.com>.

BRIDGE 101 AND THE RIVERS

Lift tower on the Hawthorne Bridge.

BRIDGE. In the English language, a bridge can be where captains command a battleship, or what dentists place in millions of mouths. We refer to the ridge on the upper part of our nose as a bridge, as we do the wedge that raises the strings of a bass fiddle above its sounding board. A bridge both separates and holds together the lenses in a pair of spectacles. It is the term scientists use when citing the bond between two or more molecules. Bridge can be Contract or Auction, as in a game of cards, and in a 32-bar jazz chorus, it is the third group of eight bars. We make a bridge of our hand, a solid arch steadying our chances with a cue. Bridge is the term for a platform over a stage that can be raised and lowered, or describes a passage in a scene or play, as the bridge from prologue to first act in *Taming of the Shrew*. Electricians, both residential and commercial, bridge circuits in a two-branch network, and we sometimes hurry along sidewalks sheltered by scaffolding, bridge-like protection from high-rise construction and falling debris.

Burnside Bridge during reconstruction, ca. 1926. Steel Bridge in background.

In the time of mythic Norse heroes, Valhalla, a heavenly habitat with 540 doors, was connected to earth by a rainbow that served as a bridge between the here and hereafter. Another Germanic legend holds that at harvest time the Emperor Charlemagne may be seen on a moonbeam bridge from which he blesses the crops:

> The moon doth brightly shine
> And buildeth a bridge of gold
> Across the emerald Rhine

To "burn one's bridges" means to commit oneself to a course of action without possibility of backing down. This saying comes from ancient military times when soldiers crossing a river literally burned the bridge they had used in order to cut off any means of retreat. Then there are the legendary devils' bridges and saints' bridges, and the old and new bridges made of love.

The Portland Bridge Book, except in the case of poetry, mostly stays away from metaphor, limiting itself to concrete, steel, and the big bridges that provide passage over rivers, chasms, and roads at the beginning of the 21st century. According to the U.S. Federal Highway Administration, this type of bridge is defined as "any span or structure across an opening 20 feet or greater." Oregon, with its countless creeks, gullies, canyons, rivers, and ravines, is crisscrossed with nearly 7,000 city, county, and state-owned public highway bridges. There are almost 600,000 highway bridges in the U.S.—not counting pedestrian-only bridges, privately owned bridges, and bridges owned by utilities, the U.S. Forest Service, or railroads.

The state with the most highway bridges is Texas—nearly 50,000 spans. Most bridges are not over water, but part of interstate and intrastate highway systems. Thus, Texas, with the most miles of pavement, boasts the greatest number of highway bridges in the U.S.

Among Oregon's vast and wonderful bridge collections are the monumental Conde B. McCullough bridges along Oregon Coast Highway 101; 50 covered bridges (the fifth largest collection of covered bridges in the U.S.); the triple arches across Crooked River Gorge in Central Oregon; the reinforced concrete deck arch and truss bridges of the Columbia River Gorge; and Portland's 12 highway bridges concentrated on the Willamette River between Kelley Point and Oregon City, plus the Sauvie Island Bridge across the Multnomah Channel of the Willamette. These 13, along with two Oregon-Washington bridges across the Columbia River and four large railroad-only bridges, serve as the subjects of *The Portland Bridge Book* and are described in detail.

The Willamette River highway bridges are presented in geographical order, beginning with the St. Johns at Willamette River mile 5.8

(river mile 0 is between Sauvie Island and Kelley Point at the confluence of the Willamette with the Columbia River). Moving south (upstream) are the Fremont, Broadway, Steel, Burnside, Morrison, Hawthorne, Marquam, Ross Island, Sellwood, Abernethy, and, finally, the Oregon City Bridge at river mile 25.9. The Sauvie Island Bridge, located across the Multnomah Channel of the Willamette River, is ten miles northwest of downtown Portland. Interstate 5 and Glenn L. Jackson bridges cross the Columbia River at river miles 106.5 and 112.4, respectively. Included also are railroad bridges—one each on the Columbia and Oregon Slough, and two on the Willamette.

Throughout the Portland area there are many other bridges worthy of note, but because they do not cross the Willamette or Columbia rivers they are not, with the exception of Sauvie Island, chapter headings in this book. One example is the very important Balch Gulch Bridge on Thurman Street in Northwest Portland, built for the 1905 Lewis and Clark Exposition. One of about 150 highway and pedestrian bridges owned and maintained by the City of Portland, this unusual hanging deck truss is the oldest highway deck truss bridge in Oregon, and one of the state's only two remaining pin-connected deck trusses. Other fascinating bridges excluded are the Vista Avenue Viaduct, a 248-foot open-spandrel reinforced concrete highway arch located 128 feet above S.W. Jefferson Street on the way to U.S. Highway 26 in Portland's West Hills; the McLoughlin Bridge (one of two Portland metropolitan-area spans designed by McCullough) over the Clackamas River near Oregon City; the bridges across the Banfield I-84 Freeway; and the bridges of McLoughlin Avenue and Barbur Boulevard.

On many of the field trips I lead for schools, I begin by asking students and the adult chaperones, "How long will it take, all of us on a big yellow school bus, to drive completely around Portland, making the loop between Fremont Bridge (I-405), to the north, and Marquam Bridge (I-5), to the south?" The answer is usually "hours and hours."

Before we set our stop watch, I ask a second question: "Remembering the definition of a bridge, during the time we make our circle, how many bridges will the tires of this school bus touch, or will we pass over, or drive beneath?" Our best time, never going over the speed limit or trying this during rush hour? Seven minutes, 58 seconds. The number of bridges we count that are 20 feet or longer? More than 40.

It is true that other cities can claim greater numbers of big river bridges. More than 12 bridges link the Golden Triangle in downtown Pittsburgh; however, all are fixed-span bridges—none have movable spans. New York City owns 860 bridges of all types, including eight bridges across the Harlem River and four large East River bridges, but it is a mile from the Manhattan Bridge to the Williamsburg Bridge, and more than three miles from Williamsburg to the Queensboro Bridge. Portland's Central City Willamette River bridges are only 1/3 mile apart, with five of them safe and legal for pedestrians and bicyclists. In abbreviated space, Portland has the world's only telescoping double-deck vertical lift bridge, the country's oldest operating vertical lift bridge, the world's second longest tied arch bridge, and a rare bascule that retracts at the same time it lifts—included among bridges built nearly every decade in the 20th century.

As writer, historian, and engineer Henry Petroski pointed out after a visit to Portland and its bridges in 1993, and as Eric DeLony, former Chief of the Historic American Engineering Record/National Parks Service, writes in this book's foreword, Portland is an open-air museum of bridges designed by world-class engineers. This compendium of 20th century bridge-building technology is reflected in three areas: design, use of materials, and construction methods.

Bridge 101

Three Main Bridge Types

In all the history of design, engineering, and construction, there are still only three basic types of bridges: arch, suspension, and beam, or truss. Structurally, a beam and a truss bridge act the same. A truss bridge, with all its triangles, is what remains when some of the steel in a beam bridge has been cut away to save weight. (Seattle's floating bridges fit into the beam category.) Portland offers examples of all three main bridge types.

Three Main Movable Bridge Types

As there are only three basic bridge types, there also are only three main movable bridge types: the swing bridge, balanced on a central pier and rotating about a vertical axis; the vertical lift, which moves up and down in horizontal position; and the bascule (from the French word for seesaw), developed from the medieval drawbridge, which tilts upward.

BEAM/TRUSS BRIDGE: MARQUAM BRIDGE

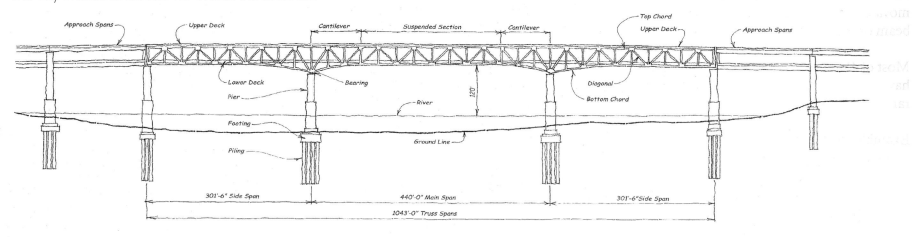

ARCH BRIDGE: FREMONT BRIDGE

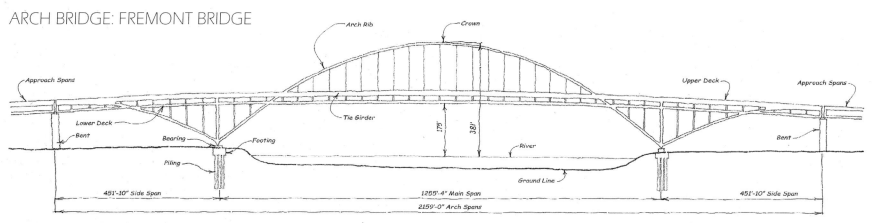

SUSPENSION BRIDGE: ST. JOHNS

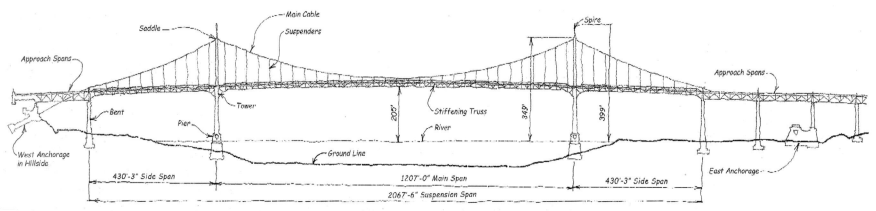

The three main bridge types: beam/truss, arch, and suspension.

4

Arch bridges and suspension bridges are rarely movable bridges, a function exclusive to the beam or truss bridge.

Most of Portland's Central City truss bridges have movable spans, as do three of the four railroad bridges included in this volume.

Examples of past and present swing span bridges in the Portland area are the former 1887 and 1905 Morrison bridges, the 1888 Steel Bridge, the 1891 and 1900 Madison spans (precursors to the extant Hawthorne Bridge), and three of the area's railroad bridges. One of the railroad swing spans, Burlington Northern Santa Fe Railway (BNSF) Bridge 5.1 at river mile 7, was rebuilt as a vertical lift span in 1989. Vertical lift highway bridges in Portland are Hawthorne, Steel, and Interstate. Examples of the bascule-type are the Broadway, Burnside, and Morrison bridges.

Engineers/Builders

This book also recognizes individual bridge engineers and their companies, as well as the contractors who built the bridges. Many are famous throughout the nation and the world. For example:

- Gustav Lindenthal, responsible for all of the Ross Island Bridge, design of Sellwood's truss spans, and construction of the Burnside Bridge, had served as New York City Commissioner of Bridges.
- Ralph Modjeski, designer of the Broadway Bridge and what are now called the BNSF 5.1, 8.8, and 9.6 railroad spans. Modjeski designed the Benjamin Franklin Bridge (opened as the Philadelphia-Camden Bridge), the longest suspension span in the world

when it opened in 1926. He also designed the Oregon Trunk Railroad Bridge opened across the Crooked River Gorge in 1911.

- David Steinman, a New York City native and an international expert on aerodynamics during the first half of the 20th century, left his mark in Oregon with the only highway suspension bridge in the Willamette Valley, the St. Johns Bridge.
- Joseph Strauss, famous for the Golden Gate Bridge, designed and held the patent for Burnside's lift.
- The firm of Waddell & Harrington, participants in the design of the northbound Interstate Bridge, also designed Steel and Hawthorne bridges, as well as bridges in the U.S., Canada, Mexico, Russia, China, Japan, and New Zealand.
- Parsons, Brinckerhoff, Quade & Douglas of New York City designed the Fremont Bridge and engineered New York's IRT and San Francisco's BART subway systems.
- Sverdrup & Parcel, designers of the Vandenburg rocket launching operation in California, designed Portland's Glenn Jackson Memorial Bridge, and worked with the Portland-based engineering firm Moffatt, Nichol & Taylor on the 1958 Morrison Bridge.
- Consulting engineers Howard, Needles, Tammen & Bergendoff (HNTB) designed Steel Bridge's RiverWalk, the new lift span for BNSF Bridge 5.1, and hundreds of other bridges nationwide.
- Three founded-in-Oregon firms have become prominent bridge engineers in recent years:
  - David Evans & Associates, designers of the 2008 Sauvie Island Bridge and engineers

for rehabilitation projects on Hawthorne, Burnside, and Broadway bridges.
  - OBEC Consulting Engineers, design engineers for rehabilitation projects on St. Johns and Burnside bridges.
  - CH2M Hill, now one of the largest engineering firms in the U.S. and designers of Hawthorne Bridge's modern east approach transition span.
- The most prolific local bridge construction company in the early years was the Pacific Bridge Co., builder of the first two bridges across the lower Willamette River, and other area spans, including some of the bridges in the Columbia River Gorge and along the Oregon Coast.

Bridge Ownership

This is a confusing subject in the Portland area, with good reason:

- Multnomah County owns four of the five large movable bridges: Hawthorne, Morrison, Burnside, and Broadway bridges, as well as Sellwood and Sauvie Island bridges.
- Oregon Department of Transportation (ODOT) owns state and interstate highway structures, i.e., Ross Island, Marquam, Fremont, St. Johns, Oregon City, and Abernethy bridges, and across the Columbia River, Glenn Jackson Bridge and, in a joint agreement with Washington state, the Interstate Bridge.
- BNSF Railway owns and operates bridges 5.1, 8.8, and 9.6 between Portland and Vancouver.
- Union Pacific Railroad owns and operates a single-track railroad bridge at Lake Oswego (former Southern Pacific Railroad Bridge), and the Steel Bridge, part of Union Pacific's main line.

- The City of Portland is in charge of traffic across the downtown street level bridges (non-freeway). Last in the business of building and operating bridges across the Willamette River in 1913, the city now owns and maintains about 150 highway and pedestrian bridges, but only two dozen cross water. These include Johnson Creek, Fanno Creek, and the Columbia Slough. Among the major city-owned highway bridges are Balch Gulch and Vista Avenue Viaduct. PDOT's RiverWalk pedestrian and bicycle sidewalk opened across the Steel Bridge in 2001. A project of Portland Parks, three large pedestrian bridges opened along the western end of the Springwater Trail Corridor in 2006. A city-built tramway, a 3,300-foot-long "aerial" bridge, is expected to open in early 2007.

Traffic

In 2006 an estimated one-half million vehicles use the downtown lower Willamette River bridges daily (from Fremont to Ross Island), with the peripheral Sauvie Island, St. Johns, Sellwood, Interstate, and Glenn Jackson bridges carrying another 330,000. Add the 117,000 on Abernethy and Oregon City bridges, and total river crossings near a million vehicles per day. Cars and trucks in our driveways and on our roads now outnumber Oregon's citizens, true since 1997 when more than four million vehicles were registered in Oregon. In 2004, Oregon's population was 3.5 million and California's almost 36 million, yet, per capita, Oregon has about the same vehicle-to-person ratio as California. Vehicular over-population holds true today on the West Coast from California to Washington: According to *State Rankings 2006*, California

has 1.15 vehicles per person and Oregon has 1.06 vehicles per person. The force of the car is not new. The "Portland Timeline," published by the City of Portland Auditor's office, shows that in 1926 Portland had more cars per capita than Chicago or New York City: "Portland makes way for the now dominant mode of transportation by widening select streets to 120 feet to serve as arterials connecting principal parts of the city." Before 1980, only 5.3 miles of bikeways had been developed in Portland. By 2000, there were 219 bikeway miles, up from 75.8 miles in 1990, and as of 2006, there are 257 miles of bikeways in the City of Portland. This includes 30 miles of bicycle boulevards, 170 miles of bicycle lanes, and 67 miles of off-street paths.

Bridge Safety

Many of Portland's bridges were designed at the cutting edge of technology for their times. Despite the age of these structures, the margin of safety for all users of Oregon's bridges is good. The public is protected from structural failure of bridges by the agencies that own them and by regular biennial inspections. The Federal Highway Administration first mandated these inspections in 1970. This was as a result of the collapse of the Silver Bridge across the Ohio River in West Virginia in 1967, which killed 46 people. One of Oregon's worst contemporary bridge disasters occurred 22 December 1964, when part of the one-year-old John Day Bridge collapsed. This four-lane highway bridge, built to carry Interstate 80N (now I-84) over the John Day River, is located approximately 1,000 feet upstream of the confluence with the Columbia River. Pier 3 washed out, taking out spans 4 and 5 during one of Oregon's worst floods. Although not a bridge failure, the worst bridge

disaster in the Portland area occurred in 1893, when a trolley motorman disregarded a red light on Madison Bridge No. 1 (a predecessor to the Hawthorne Bridge) during heavy early morning fog. As a result, the trolley car *Inez* tumbled into the Willamette's murky water and seven people drowned.

Threats to Bridge Life

In addition to earthquakes and the constant pull of gravity (engineers are always fighting heavy and falling), there are other major threats to Portland's bridges:

Floods: In recent years floods have damaged some of the downtown bridges, with Burnside's east end counterweight pit springing a leak in 1996. In this same flood, Morrison Bridge's two timber fenders (protection also called starlings or dolphins) were smashed and required repairs that cost $250,000.

Wildlife: Birds are enormously damaging to bridges. With so many spans across the lower Willamette, urban birds have nearly as many overnight choices as human tourists. Crows, starlings, and long-lived pigeons outnumber all other birds. Well-fed by the spillage of two large mid-town grain terminals, birds and their droppings create an acid that eats through paint. It is paint that prevents rusting. When bridges rust, the steel can lose its strength. (As a side note, bridges, in addition to serving as homes to peregrine falcons, also serve as bat hotels and as bat nurseries—some species raise their young in crevices found in bridges. The Oregon Department of Fish and Wildlife (ODFW) has asked ODOT to make bridges in certain areas more "bat-friendly." Of the 15 species of bats in Oregon, ODFW has documented six or seven species that regularly use bridges here, including some use by "sensitive species." As a result, ODOT now includes bat habitat in new bridge construction. For more about bats and peregrines on bridges, see <www.batcon.org> and <www.audubonportland.org>.)

Salt/Studded Tires: Salt corrodes steel, producing rust. This corrosion damages bridges in two ways. First, the steel loses strength as it rusts. Second, for rusting steel buried inside concrete, the rust expands and pops pieces of concrete off the structure—a condition called spalling. One source of salt is ocean air. The most famous Oregon bridge lost as a result of salt corrosion from ocean air was the bridge designed by Conde McCullough across Alsea Bay at Waldport, replaced in 1991. In the eastern U.S., salt spread on roads to melt ice and snow does great damage to bridges. Salt is not generally used for road maintenance in Oregon; thus bridge damage from salt is minimal in the Portland area. However, another method for coping with winter driving conditions— studded tires (legal in the West but not in the East)—is one of the great roadway surface eroders of all times. In recent years, roadway decks on numerous Portland-area bridges, including Ross Island, Hawthorne, Morrison, and Broadway, have been repaired or replaced at substantial cost due to severe traffic wear, caused largely by studded tires.

Traffic Loads: Larger and larger vehicles are using the Oregon's highways. Typical trucks now weigh up to 40 tons, nearly twice as heavy as trucks in service when many of our Portland-area bridges were designed. Heavy traffic reduces a bridge's safety margin, and can even damage the structure. Luckily for us in Portland, the Hawthorne, Burnside, and Broadway bridges were originally designed to carry streetcars, which were similar in weight to present-day trucks. Nevertheless, these sturdy bridges are now reaching their capacity for traffic loads. Away from downtown Portland, older bridges such as Sellwood and the 1950 Sauvie Island were designed only for the smaller trucks of the time, and are too light for today's traffic.

Obsolescence: A bridge is judged to be functionally obsolete if it doesn't meet today's design standards for roadway width, shoulders, overhead clearance, and other requirements for accommodating traffic with safety. In addition to being underdesigned for 21st century traffic loads, the Sellwood and 1950 Sauvie Island bridges are now designated as functionally obsolete. These two bridges are typical of many older steel

Crack repair (steel bandaid) on Sellwood Bridge concrete girder, ca. 2006.

truss bridges that are no longer big enough or heavy enough for today's traffic. In fact, steel truss bridges are declining drastically in number locally as well as nationally. As of early 2006, only about 150 truss bridges of all types or age are known to remain on Oregon's highway system among the nearly 7,000 highway bridges in inventory. Most bridges in service today are concrete or steel girders rather than steel trusses, which were more common in the past. This shift in bridge type is due to obsolescence of many old steel trusses and lower cost of concrete girder or steel girder structures for new construction. Steel trusses are relatively expensive because of the labor required to fabricate and assemble the many pieces.

Bridge Funding and Historic Bridges

Federal Highway Administration figures show that Oregon's bridge funding needs are greater than those of Alaska, Idaho, and Washington. Oregon's local agencies (cities and counties) and state agencies are held responsible for maximizing public safety while keeping bridge maintenance and repair costs to a minimum. However, funding for bridge upgrading and replacement is as unstable as sand at the turn of the tide. An extra challenge is added when the bridge is a historic structure. If a bridge more than 50 years old is deemed historically significant, it is eligible for the National Register of Historic Places. If eligible, it is protected by national preservation laws. To extend protection, in 2006, ODOT, the Advisory Council on Historic Preservation, and the Oregon State Historic Preservation Office (SHPO) signed an agreement that all canal systems, covered bridges, suspension bridges, movable bridges, arch bridges, and truss bridges that are 50 years old or older and retain integrity are considered eligible for the National Register of Historic Places.

The Interstate Bridge was determined eligible for listing in the National Register in 1984. Seven other Portland-area bridges across the Willamette and Columbia rivers were also determined eligible in 1984: Oregon City, Ross Island, Hawthorne, Burnside, Steel, Broadway and St. Johns. A few of these bridges have also been listed as Portland landmarks, and the Oregon City Bridge was officially nominated to the Register in 2005.

Whenever repair or rehabilitation work is required for an eligible bridge and federal funds are involved, the law requires a process whereby the proposed work is evaluated to determine if it might have an adverse affect. If the work is going to compromise the historic integrity of the bridge, mitigation efforts must be made to minimize the harm, or it must be determined that there is no prudent or feasible alternative. In-kind replacement of parts is a way to retain the historic character and is often a part of an extensive bridge project to meet those conditions. For example, bridge railings must be made in the same form and

The Oregon City Bridge is listed in the National Register of Historic Places.

of the same materials. The federal regulations (Section 106 of the National Historic Preservation Act of 1966, and Section 4(f) of the Department of Transportation Act of 1966) are related to federal funding. There may be times when a bridge cannot be saved because of safety concerns, and the process becomes complex. If no federal funds are involved, it is up to the local agency (city or county) to meet its own regulations. When the Hawthorne Bridge was closed for one year in 1998-99 for a $21 million rehabilitation that included federal funds, it was determined that the proposed changes in the bridge's appearance would have an "adverse effect" on its historic integrity. As mitigation for this

effect, ODOT documented the bridge with photographs prior to the reconstruction work.

Multnomah County's four movable bridges are among the largest mechanical structures in the United States, yet each year maintenance and capital needs far outweigh funding.

ODOT is faced with the same or greater challenges. Its six lower Willamette River bridges (St. Johns, Fremont, Marquam, Ross Island, Abernethy, and Oregon City) are only a few of the 2,633 Oregon highway bridges owned outright by ODOT, with about 850 ODOT bridges now approaching the end of their design life. As with Multnomah County,

ODOT's regular funding level is not enough to maintain its bridges in their current condition. In 2001 Mark Hirota, then Oregon State Bridge Engineer, estimated that Oregonians would have to invest more than $100 million annually in bridge work through 2020, almost double what was being invested in 2001. To avoid a crisis with the state's highways and bridges, the 2001 Oregon Legislature passed the Oregon Transportation Investment Act, known as OTIA I. The act increased driver and motor vehicle fees to secure bonds for transportation funding, including $130 million for repair and replacement of bridges. In 2002, OTIA II added $45 million for more bridge work. OTIA I and II together funded 55 projects on bridges owned by cities, counties and the state. In 2003, ODOT issued a report describing how hundreds of Oregon's concrete bridges built in the 1940s and 1950s were showing serious signs of aging and deterioration. In response, the 2003 Legislature passed OTIA III. This massive funding program was designed to provide $1.3 billion to repair or replace more than 300 state highway bridges and $300 million to repair or replace about 150 city and county bridges. Significant amounts of OTIA funds are helping finance work on Portland-area bridges, including the new Sauvie Island Bridge.

Seismic Retrofit, or Shaky Ground

Dollars are scarce in ODOT's and Multnomah County's seismic retrofit funds. Seismic retrofit means to strengthen already-built bridges against earthquake. For just the County's six Willamette River bridges, this need is estimated to be, in 2004 dollars, about $129 million. To date, the only retrofitting has been partial retrofitting of the Burnside Bridge, this

Lift bridge towers are vulnerable to earthquakes.

despite concerns about the vulnerability of Oregon bridges to earthquake, especially since the "Spring Break" quake in March 1993. By the end of 2000, ODOT had retrofitted Marquam Bridge only, with a contract for some strengthening of the Abernethy Bridge underway. Statewide, ODOT had retrofitted or was in the process of retrofitting about 150 of its bridges, with retrofit of 1,600 more on the "need to fix, but waiting for funding" list.

Maps produced by Metro and the Oregon Department of Geology and Mineral Industries show that vast areas in Portland are earthquake sensitive, especially along the waterfront. How ground responds to shaking, thus determining the stability of people and things on that ground, depends on three conditions: loose soils (amplifies/increases ground motion), liquefaction (changes loose soil into liquid matter), and slope (the steeper the ground, the greater the landslide). Areas with the greatest earthquake risk are shown on the "Earthquake Hazards" maps in red. All the riverbanks and the bridges along the waterfront sit in the red zone. Portland sits atop three main faults. One of them, 30 miles long, runs along the northern edge of Forest Park and along the foot of Portland's West Hills before turning east on West Burnside and then passes through the center of downtown.

At the time the Willamette River bridges were built, earthquakes were not seen as a threat. Also, engineers had not yet developed methods for designing and building bridges to resist seismic forces. All Willamette River bridges built before the Morrison Bridge (1958) are supported on timber piles or footings that sit on gravel in water ranging from 30 to 90 feet deep. Only Portland's later bridges were built with steel piles. Most bridge approaches on both sides of the river are located on landfills. This is not good news since engineers now know that earthquakes can cause improperly built landfills to "liquefy," which can cause the ground to settle, or sink. Also, soft landfill materials can displace horizontally when liquefied, a condition called lateral spreading. Settling and lateral spreading can be disastrous to older bridges.

The American Association of State Highway and Transportation Officials (AASHTO) Code governs bridge design, with additional requirements imposed in Oregon by ODOT. AASHTO and ODOT now better understand the risks earthquakes pose to bridge structures and have extensive analysis and design requirements for new bridges to increase their resistance to seismic forces. However, it is not economically feasible to go back and strengthen all existing bridges to meet these requirements. Therefore, ODOT has adopted a two-phased approach for retrofitting Oregon's most critical bridges. First, these bridges are being retrofitted to tie the superstructures to the support piers. This "Phase 1" retrofitting addresses the biggest potential earthquake threat: separation of the superstructure from the piers, leading to collapse. Later, as funding becomes available, additional "Phase 2" retrofitting will be done to strengthen the support piers, or the bridges will be replaced with new bridges designed to resist current code-mandated earthquake loads.

One key step in ODOT's seismic design program was to develop guidelines for bridges at specific locations around the state. The guidelines use a series of Peak Ground Acceleration maps produced by the U.S. Geological Survey (USGS) for each state.

The maps provide information to determine the severity of seismic forces for new bridge designs as well as retrofits.

While all bridges are vulnerable, movable bridges, due to their suspended counterweights, require more complicated, thus expensive, seismic retrofit solutions. On the Morrison Bridge, for example, concrete girders rather than steel beams support the entire opening apparatus (each highway deck leaf weighing 1,600 tons). These girders could be damaged in a major earthquake. In 1995, the City of Portland completed a seismic risk analysis of all 133 city-owned bridges, ranking each according to vulnerability and importance to the public. Of these, 89 lacked adequate structural details to meet new earthquake codes. During the summer of 1997, the city completed the Phase 1 seismic upgrade for the 12th Avenue Bridge over I-84, near Benson High School in Northeast Portland. Design has been completed for a seismic upgrade of the Going Street overpass to Swan Island. Construction is expected to start in 2007 at a cost of $4.3 million. Other bridges at the top of the city's priority list include two eastbound approaches to the Steel Bridge, and a Phase 1 retrofit for the N.E. 33rd Avenue Bridge over N.E. Columbia Blvd. This was originally scheduled to begin in January 1998. Again, construction stopped for lack of funding. In 2005, the City of Portland estimated its seismic strengthening program at $50 million.

By comparison, Caltrans, California's Department of Transportation, is spending billions on seismic retrofit of its bridges, with $6 billion alone being spent to earthquake-proof the San Francisco-Oakland Bay Bridge at the turn of the 21st century.

The Rivers

The first Portland expressways were the rivers. These ocean-going "freeways" looping through our midst were the only expedient routes for carrying goods, people, and services in and carrying goods, people, and services out. In the days before dams, the Willamette and Columbia were trickier delivery systems. Spring and other freshets fouled first floors of buildings (and sometimes the second). Travelers thought twice about the pull of tide between St. Johns and Sellwood. Could you get home before nightfall, or before next Wednesday? Did you have the fare, or want to trust those exploding steamboats? In that time before cobblestone and asphalt, we drank out of the rivers, washed clothes in the rivers, dumped sewage in the rivers, tanned hides by the rivers, and more.

Bridges came. More bridges were built, higher bridges part of Interstate freeways—a multitude of ways to get above the rivers, away from the rivers. Just as well, as the Willamette River grew sluggish and stinky and turned funky green and black, "strangled" for lack of oxygen in the 1940s.

Now, the bottom deck of the Fremont, the North Star of downtown Portland commuting geography, clears the Willamette by 175 feet. The main span of the St. Johns Bridge—farther down the Willamette—tops Fremont's clearance by an additional 30 feet. The average main span elevation for the non-freeway bridges located across the Willamette between the Broadway and the Oregon City bridges is more than 70 feet. When crossing the rivers, ignoring the rivers might be one of the largest daily shared urban experiences.

The Willamette River makes a 45-degree bend between the Burnside and Steel bridges.

Yet the Willamette and Columbia and the bridges that cross them invite contemplation. In the last ten years, ever-increasing numbers of bicyclists have lobbied successfully for their own lanes on nearly all of the spans. With so many wheels, a bridge can be a formidable geometry for the walker who stands still to look over a railing. Unless counting bridges from the sidewalks on top of the Morrison Bridge, it is not easy to see the river's 45-degree bend between the Burnside and Steel bridges. How many of us stand on the dock at Albers Mill to check which way the Willamette's headed? Here in the last dozen miles of all the drainage from the Willamette basin, the river often looks like a plugged bathtub, with tides noticeably pushing the river's flow back toward Oregon City, especially during low water.

It is not obvious that while the Central City gentrifies, the Willamette is still a working river, with islands of gravel, chip barges, grain ships, tugs, dredges, cranes, and waterfront terminals. However, the log rafts and barges that ran all the way upriver to Salem have gone the way of stumps, shingle mills, and sourdough biscuits mixed in the top of flour sacks and cooked over an open camp fire.

Founded in 1891, the Port of Portland is prominent on the lower Willamette, the biggest ships now calling below the Broadway Bridge, north of the Central City waterfront. According to latest figures, the Port's four active marine cargo terminals handle about 12 million tons of cargo per year. This includes autos, agricultural and forest products, grain, mineral bulks, and containerized goods. It is one of the country's top four points of entry for autos and the number one port for export of U.S. wheat. Portland is also the leading West Coast tonnage port for automobiles and bulk products, surpassing both Long Beach and Los Angeles. The Port expects to make 125,000 containerized moves in 2006.

If this edition were to include a glossary of river-related words (for this you must refer to the second edition of *The Portland Bridge Book*), it would say the 1,200-mile-long Columbia River rises from Lake Columbia in British Columbia and drains more than 220,000 square miles of land from the Rocky Mountains west to the Pacific Ocean. The Columbia basin includes all of southeastern British Columbia, more than half of Washington state, all of Oregon and Idaho, and some of Nevada. Its major tributaries (in order of discharge) include the Snake, Willamette, Kootenai, Pend Oreille, Cowlitz, and Spokane rivers. There are 11 hydroelectric dams on the Columbia in the U.S. and three in Canada. Captain Robert Gray named the river in 1792 for his ship, the *Columbia Rediviva.*

The Willamette is 187 miles long, runs south to north between the Coast and Cascade ranges, and is the defining natural feature of the largest city in Oregon. The Willamette and its tributaries form the Willamette Valley basin. The river rises in the high Cascades in Douglas County to flow into the Columbia

River at Kelley Point, about 12 miles northwest of downtown Portland, which is about 90 miles east of the Pacific Ocean. Portland is one of a handful of inland river port cities in the U.S. called on by ocean-going vessels. Tributaries include the Coast Fork, Middle Fork, Long Tom River, Row River, McKenzie River, Fall Creek, Blue River, Luckiamute, Santiam, and the Clackamas—the latter a vital infusion of clean water into the lower Willamette. There are 13 dams on the river's tributaries: Fern Ridge, Cottage Grove, Dorena, Big Cliff, Detroit, Dexter, Lookout Point, Hills Creek, Cougar, Fall Creek, Foster, Green Peter, and Blue River. They were built between 1949 and 1969. Of these, 11 are still used for flood control and two for hydroelectric power. Part of the Willamette's flood plain was designated as a National Natural Landmark in 1987 and the river itself was named an American Heritage River in 1997. Portland Harbor, a federally designated Superfund site, still has many problems, but it's come a long ways since Portland's earlier years.

Portland bridges and their reasons for being are a large topic. *The Portland Bridge Book* places each structure in relation to the others: how many vehicles travel daily across each of them, what colors they are painted, whether pedestrians and bicycles are allowed on them, how high and wide they are, what they cost, and if they are movables, how many long and short toots from radioless river craft will get them to open. Placement of the Portland bridges, past and present, speaks to the political planning and maneuvering for constructing the city of Portland. Each is given historical context, with explanations of what was happening around them at the time each opened and what is taking place around them at the turn of the millennium. A few connect highways to Mount Hood, to the Oregon Coast, and to states and counties north and south. The Central City Waterfront bridges, however, lead the traveler to Portland's New Chinatown/Japantown and Skidmore/Old Town, Union Station, Oregon Convention Center and the Lloyd District, Tom McCall and Eastbank Esplanade, Saturday Market, the River District, Hawthorne Boulevard and the Central Eastside Industrial District, Oregon Museum of Science and Industry, marinas and moorages, and the rest of the world.

WILLAMETTE
by Stephen Maybell (*Native Sun* Magazine, Portland, 1911)

There's a bank by the waves of the blue Willamette

Where the zephyr weaves many a song;

Where the tall, waving pine shades the violet,

And the little birds sing the day long,

Where, up from the moss beds through ferns into space,

The vines reach the mystic forever;

And the pale water lily looks down on her face

In the depths of that beautiful river.

When the angels of heaven draw this curtain of light,

And reveal the dark regions of space,

When we gaze on the marvelous splendor of night,

And trace the great Infinite's face!

There's a harp in the air though its music be mute;

Threre's a song in the silence unsung;

There are forms, though loneliness reigns absolute

That speak—yet not found of a tongue.

And I've stood in the lilac's dark shadows alone,

By the gleam of that star-fettered river,

When the shades had a touch, and the stillness a tone,

Whose music shall haunt me forever.

CONSTRUCTION HISTORY OF PORTLAND-AREA RIVER BRIDGES

YEAR OPENED	BRIDGE NAME	LIFT TYPE	BRIDGE TYPE
1887	*Morrison*	S	Truss
1888	*Oregon City**	FS	Suspension
1888	*Steel*	S	Truss
1891	*Madison #1*	S	Truss
1894	*Burnside*	S	Truss
1900	*Madison #2*	S	Truss
1905	*Morrison*	S	Truss
1908	*BNSF 5.1*	S	Truss
1908	BNSF 8.8	S	Truss
1908	BNSF 9.6	S	Truss
1910	UP	FS	Truss
1910	Hawthorne	VL	Truss
1912	Steel	VL	Truss
1913	Broadway	B	Truss
1917	Interstate (northbound)	VL	Truss
1922	Oregon City	FS	Arch
1925	Sellwood	FS	Truss
1926	Burnside	B	Truss
1926	Ross Island	FS	Truss
1931	St. Johns	FS	Suspension
1950	Sauvie Island (original)	FS	Truss
1958	Morrison	B	Truss
1958	Interstate (southbound)	VL	Truss
1966	Marquam	FS	Truss
1970	Abernethy/l-205	FS	Truss
1973	Fremont	FS	Arch
1982	Glenn L. Jackson	FS	Beam
1989	BNSF 5.1	VL	Truss
2008	Sauvie Island (new)	FS	Arch

Glenn Jackson Bridge.

* Pedestrian bridge only

Italics designate removed bridges.

FIXED SPAN (FS) = 12
SWING (S) = 9
VERTICAL LIFT (VL) = 5
BASCULE (B) = 3
BNSF = Burlington Northern Santa Fe Railway
UP = Union Pacific Railroad

ST. JOHNS BRIDGE

ST. JOHNS
river mile 5.8

Opened
13 June 1931

Structure Types
Two-tower steel cable suspension bridge with
half-through Warren stiffening trusses. Steel
Warren deck truss approach spans.

Main Span Length
1,207 feet

Center Height to Water
205 feet

Tower Height to Water
400 feet

Outside Width
50 feet
(four traffic lanes with two 5-foot sidewalks)

Color
verdant green

Cost
$3.9 million
major rehabilitation 2003-2005, $43 million

Owner
ODOT, since 1976;
built by Multnomah County

Design Engineers
David B. Steinman and Holton Robinson,
New York

Access
pedestrians, bicycles allowed

Average Daily Traffic
24,500

Historic American Engineering Record
OR-40

T HE WILLAMETTE VALLEY'S ONLY MAJOR SUSPENSION BRIDGE, the
St. Johns is the symbolic marine gateway to Portland. At the time of its opening in 1931,
it had the longest span of any suspension bridge west of Detroit's Ambassador Bridge.
Farthest downstream of Portland's Willamette River bridges, located at about river mile 6, it is
a little more than seven miles from downtown Portland. It connects the distant North Portland
communities of St. Johns (east end) and Linnton (west). In 2004, almost 25,000 vehicles crossed
the Willamette at this point each day, making St. Johns one of the least traveled of the lower
Willamette River highway bridges.

This graceful bridge is a designated Portland Historical Landmark and is eligible for the National
Register of Historic Places. It had anything but peaceful beginnings. In 1924, advocates for the

St. Johns formed the Peninsula Bridge Co., during the height of Portland's "bridge fever" years, when the Oregon City (1922), Sellwood (1925), Burnside (1926), and Ross Island (1926) bridges were opened. More than 26,000 Portlanders signed the petition for the St. Johns, touching off a five-year battle with those who thought North Portland's "Peninsula" too sparsely populated to justify such an expensive structure. Homeowners of the day paid an average of $50 a year in property taxes, and many were opposed to the $4.25 million bond issue that would raise their taxes five cents for every dollar of assessed valuation. Proponents campaigned that the St. Johns Ferry, though it carried more than 1,000 vehicles a day in its heyday, was inadequate for the area's growing industrialized economy.

Voters approved the St. Johns Bridge in November 1928, and construction began just one month before "Black Thursday," the 24 October 1929 stock market crash. The nation faced the Great Depression, when even Tillamook cheese, advertised at 17 cents a pound, was beyond the means of many out-of-work Portlanders. Those employed to build the bridge counted themselves fortunate. For a look at the bridge under construction and its early appearance, go no farther than the St. Johns Burgerville, located at the east end of the bridge on North Ivanhoe Street. A photographic triptych (each panel measuring 3'x5') and another large-scale photograph (3'x2') enhance the dining room walls.

Pastimes of the day included such activities as listening to Burns and Allen on the radio, swimming at Jantzen Beach Amusement Park (in wool Jantzen swimsuits advertised locally at $2.85 for "men, women, and children"), or rendezvousing at Swan Island Municipal Airport—Portland's first commercial field and a favorite parking spot for "neckers." (The St. Johns was only two and a half miles downriver from the 150-acre site of the Swan Island Airport, which opened in 1927 and closed in 1940.)

West approach viaduct and roadway with tower construction in the background.

Walkways for access to main cables during construction.

Main cables and suspender cables ready for installation of bridge deck.

West tower as viewed from the ground.

The St. Johns was dedicated 13 June 1931, the highlight of Portland's 23rd Rose Festival. Residents of the area at the time reported seeing biplanes fly under the bridge during the opening ceremonies. Because of its proximity to the Swan Island field, the first proposed color scheme for the bridge was selected with airplanes in mind. Aviation authorities and government officials wanted the span to be painted with yellow and black stripes, bumblebee fashion. County commissioners, reportedly "flabbergasted," disregarded the advice, waiting until St. Patrick's Day—two months before the bridge opened—to announce the St. Johns would be painted green.

"It is the ethical duty of the builders to make bridges beautiful as well as useful," said design engineer David B. Steinman, who had to make the St. Johns' deck high enough to accommodate the masts of vessels heading upstream. The majority of Portland's population agreed with Steinman. Still, they did not approve another bridge over the Willamette in Portland for over a quarter of a century, when the creaky swing-span Morrison, built in 1905, was finally replaced in 1958. (A bridge to Sauvie Island, about four miles downriver from the St. Johns Bridge, across the Multnomah Channel of the Willamette River, opened in 1950.)

Name—The bridge is named for the community at its east end, which honors settler James Johns (1809-86), variously described as a "hermit and recluse," "old Jimmy Johns," and "Saint Johns," the latter probably for his work on behalf of early schools. His grave is marked "Friend of Education." He is buried in Lot 6, Block 120, Pioneer Columbia Cemetery in North Portland.

Bridge Statistics—The St. Johns is a two-tower cable suspension bridge with a steel superstructure. It is one of only three public highway suspension bridges in all of Oregon. Its highway deck (one center span and two side spans that total 2,067 feet in length) hangs from two 2,645-foot-long suspension cables. All are supported by the bridge's twin 400-foot Gothic arch towers and anchorages, which resist the cable pull of 8,500 tons. Lines of stiffening trusses, running along both sides of the bridge's flexible deck, give the structure rigidity. (The original Tacoma Narrows Bridge was built without the stiffening truss feature. It collapsed in 1940. (See Galloping Gertie in glossary.)

On the east end, beneath the bridge in Cathedral Park, is a 29,000-ton cable anchorage. It is designed with hollow chambers to allow the ends of the bridge cables and anchor chains to be inspected. The west anchorage is inside two sloping tunnels 85 feet deep in the hillside's dense basaltic rock. The concrete above ground in both anchorages is treated with mouldings and relief to harmonize with the architectural design of the main piers.

In 1975, 34 frayed suspender cables (the vertical hangers) on the then nearly half-century-old St. Johns were replaced at a cost of about $250,000. Multnomah County owned and maintained the St. Johns from the year it was built until 1976, when the state of Oregon assumed responsibility. In 1994, the east approaches and east side span were repainted. In 1995, the main cable was unwrapped and checked for the first time since 1931. This led to a two-year $43 million rehabilitation project, completed in 2005. Most of this design work was done by ODOT. OBEC Consulting Engineers of Eugene did the design work for the cables. ODOT's lead contractor on the rehab, Max J. Kuney Co. of Spokane, Washington, replaced about 100 of the suspender cables, wrapped the main cables, and upgraded and repaired some of the bridge's steel members. After removing the old lead-based paint, the entire superstructure was repainted by Long Painting of Seattle and

Inspection of main cable, 1995.

Monumental view of Gothic arches from Cathedral Park.

19

Reel of cable strand being unloaded from truck at bridge construction site.

Cable anchor unit that will secure the main suspension cable for the bridge.

Portland. In addition, the entire concrete deck was removed and replaced, and the electrical system upgraded, with the street lighting across the bridge replaced with historically correct lampposts. Seismic and stability features were added to the main suspension span, as well as a new traffic signal at the west end of the bridge.

Engineers/Builders—The St. Johns Bridge was designed by consulting engineers David B. Steinman and Holton D. Robinson of New York City, and built under the authority of the Multnomah County commissioners. The steel was fabricated by Wallace Bridge and Steel Co. of Seattle. Gilpin Constuction Co., contractor for the Sellwood Bridge (1925), was the main contractor.

David B. Steinman (1886-1960) was born in New York City, where he attended evening high school. He received a doctorate from Columbia University in 1911. He then went to the University of Idaho as a professor of civil

engineering. He began his bridge engineering career in New York as an assistant to Gustav Lindenthal, the world-famous designer of New York City's East River Hell Gate arch bridge (1917). (For more on Lindenthal, see Burnside, Broadway, Ross Island, Sellwood, bridges, and glossary.) Steinman was also a prolific writer. One of his most famous books was *Bridges and Their Builders*, written with Sara Ruth Watson and first published in 1941. Steinman eventually dominated the American bridge-building scene. His other famous bridges are: the Henry Hudson Bridge (1936), then the longest hingeless arch and the longest plate girder arch span in the world; the Thousand Islands International Bridge (1938), over the St. Lawrence River; and the Mackinac Strait Bridge (1957), Mackinaw City-St. Ignace, Michigan. The prototype for St. Johns Bridge is the Mount Hope Bridge (1929), in Rhode Island. Also designed by Steinman and Robinson, Mount Hope was recognized by the American Institute of Steel Construction with a first prize for the most "artistic" bridge the year it opened.

Unusual Note—The St. Johns' suspension cables were spun by John A. Roebling's Sons Co., of Brooklyn Bridge (1883) fame, at its Trenton, New Jersey plant. (Roebling also contracted the work for the first bridge at Oregon City, 1888, a pedestrian suspension span.) Usually the cables are spun in place with parallel wires, but the wires for the St. Johns were spun at the plant into 182 individual rope strands that were prestressed to a uniform tension, cut to a predetermined length, socketed and reeled on large wooden spools, and shipped by steamer to Portland. Each individual rope strand weighed about six and a half tons, so when 91 were assembled to make each finished main cable, that cable totaled about one and one-third million pounds.

Approaches—East end: Philadelphia Street. West end: St. Helens Road (U.S. Highway 30).

Neighborhood Landmarks—Off the bridge's steep east bank is St. Johns, a

St. Johns Bridge looking north.

community of 13,000, originally settled in 1847. (Population of the North Portland Peninsula, according to 2000 figures, is about 57,000.) Beneath the bridge's east end is Cathedral Park, named for the Gothic architecture of the approach spans' bridge piers and the shadows cast by them. These piers range from 22 to 155 feet high. Cathedral Park, formally honored by the American Society of Landscape Architects, was created through the initial efforts of 13 determined residents who insisted that the area's waterfront be saved for public use. After nearly a decade of fundraising, the 17.5-acre park opened on 3 May 1980. As part of the dedication ceremonies, a time capsule was buried in the park's Memory Garden Wall; it is scheduled to be opened on 3 May 2030.

The St. Johns' west approach abuts St. Helens Road (U.S. Highway 30), a main thoroughfare between Portland and points north along the west side of the Columbia River. Looking from east to west across the bridge, the illusion is that the St. Johns abruptly dead ends at Forest Park and its 5,000 acres of natural woodlands. Forest Park and the community of Linnton—less populated even than St. Johns—are natural companions for this reclusive and rare bridge.

FREMONT BRIDGE

FREMONT
river mile 11.1

Opened
15 November 1973

Structure Types
Steel three-span half-through tied arch with orthotropic steel upper deck. Steel box girder approach spans.

Main Span Length
1,255 feet

Center Height to Water
175 feet (lower deck)

Top of Arch to Water
381 feet

Outside Width
81 feet (four traffic lanes each deck)

Color
"celery" green

Cost
$82 million (including approaches and $5.5 million repair cost after girder crack)

Owner
ODOT

Design Engineers
Parsons, Brinckerhoff, Quade & Douglas, New York;
Werner Storch and Assoc., Portland (concept)

Access
no pedestrians or bicycles

Average Daily Traffic
112,600

Historic American Engineering Record
OR-104

FIVE MILES UP THE WILLAMETTE from the St. Johns Bridge is the imposing Fremont. Located at river mile 11.1, this bridge bounds the river within full view of city center. The top of the rainbow arch, decorated with Oregon and American flags, is 381 feet above water level and is clearly visible from each side of the Willamette, up and down the river. The Fremont's main span, that distance between its supports, is 1,255 feet, making it the longest bridge structure on the Oregon state highway system. The Astoria-Megler Bridge across the Columbia River is the longest structure overall on the highway system, measuring 4.18 miles, but its main span, at 1,232 feet, is just short of the Fremont's main span. Fremont was the longest arch bridge of its type in the world until the Caiyuanba Bridge, with a main span of 1,378 feet, opened across the Yangtze River in Chongqing, China in August 2004.

West bearings of the Fremont Bridge.

West side span during assembly, 1971.

West side span nearly complete, before crack, 1971.

Falsework (scaffolding) where Ed Wortman and crew were working when bridge cracked

Crack

Crack in Fremont Bridge west side span tie girder, 1971.

Finished in 1973, Fremont was the third built in the computer era of Portland-area behemoth freeway bridges, following the Marquam (1966) and the Abernethy (1970). Nonetheless, it is inspected more frequently than the other bridges. On 28 October 1971, midway through construction, a crack appeared on the west side span of the structure in the south tie girder at the juncture of the arch rib. According to a state of Oregon report: "At this time the contractor had completed the erection of the west side backspan and was in the process of releasing the supporting jacks at the intermediate false works (sic) supporting the span. The north tie girder did not crack." The report continued: "The crack in the tie girder originated in the juncture piece and extended part way through both the web plates of the girder. At this time, the girder had come to rest on the false work, thus avoiding the complete failure of the backspan."

Experts debated the exact cause of the cracking. Because of the magnitude of the welding required, "locked-in stresses" may have resulted, making the steel brittle. Engineers redesigned and strengthened the defective joint and, at the same time, reinforced three other similar joints on the bridge. That fault, as well as an ironworker strike and on- and off-ramp disputes, delayed the bridge's opening nearly two years. The repair costs, about $5.5 million, were absorbed mostly by the federal government, which financed 92 percent of the total cost of the Fremont and its approaches: $82 million. Craft workers on Fremont Bridge included carpenters, ironworkers, laborers, pipefitters, and operating engineers. All the ironworkers on Fremont belonged to the International Association of Bridge, Structural, Ornamental & Reinforcing Iron Workers, Local 29, with offices in Northeast Portland.

When the Fremont was built, interstate highway system policy banned pedestrians on any part of the bridge; consequently, there are no sidewalks. That policy has since changed—the 1982 Glenn Jackson Bridge across the Columbia, for example, has a center median just for pedestrians and bicyclists. In response to requests by residents statewide who wanted a firsthand look at the Fremont before it opened to traffic, "People's Day" was declared 11 November 1973. About 30,000 persons packed the double-deck bridge for a legal pedestrian look. Four days later the Fremont opened for vehicles.

The Oregon Highway Division reported that on its first full day of operation, the bridge carried 35,350 vehicles, relieving the Broadway, Steel, and Morrison bridges of 22,000 vehicles. By 2000 it carried 109,200 vehicles daily and in 2004, 112,600. The Fremont, with its westside freeway connections, was the death knell of Harbor Drive along downtown Portland's west bank of the Willamette. That six-lane expressway was closed in 1974 and its asphalt removed to be replaced by Tom McCall Waterfront Park.

At the time of Fremont's construction, President Nixon's Watergate scandal was a household word, Tom McCall was Oregon's governor, and Portland's first bike plan was developed.

Crack inside Fremont Bridge tie girder, 1971.

Removing cracked girder over Front Avenue, 1972.

Fremont center span floated upriver to bridge location.

Fremont Bridge center span lift, March 1973.

Name—The Fremont takes its name from Fremont Street, which at one time was slated to be the eastside approach to the bridge. The street was named for John Charles Frémont (1813-90), explorer and army officer. The man—like the bridge—benefited from federal money. After serving as a railroad surveyor in the army, Frémont obtained federal aid and permission for a western journey to survey the Oregon Trail. He is buried in Pierpont on the Hudson, New York.

Bridge Statistics—The Fremont is a tied arch orthotropic deck bridge designed without pier supports in the main channel. Fremont incorporates arch span and box girder designs. Because the roadway passes through the arch of the bridge, it is known as a "through-arch" span. The tied arches carry the vertical load and horizontal girders. In turn, the girders carry the orthotropic deck (roadway) and act as tension ties for the arches. In effect, the bridge is a carefully balanced spring, with the three-span continuous arch ribs, the tie and stiffening girders, and the four piers mutually supporting one another. The steel plate upper deck is designed with strengthening properties in two directions, thus "orthotropic." The orthotropic upper deck carries westbound traffic, and a conventional concrete lower deck, suspended

from the upper deck, carries eastbound traffic. Its orthotropic deck employs an elegant and utilitarian engineering technique developed in Europe after the Second World War when steel was scarce. State-of-the-art in its era, the design of the Fremont keeps dead weight to a minimum and allows this unusually long bridge to carry its own weight.

The Fremont's 902-foot center span section was fabricated in California, but assembled at Swan Island, 1.7 miles downstream from Fremont's site. Engineers from all over the world came to watch the 6,000-ton center span (after it was floated up the Willamette on two barges) hoisted 175 feet into place in a 50-hour lift. This was accomplished using 32 hydraulic jacks, eight at each corner, and was the heaviest bridge lift ever up until that time.

Engineers/Builders—Fremont, including approaches, was built in seven sections between 1968 and 1973. Its design, however, was a result of the public's reaction to Marquam Bridge, designed by ODOT and opened in 1966. Many people, including the Portland Art Commission (PAC), were unhappy with Marquam's double-deck truss mass across

The Fremont's center span section is lifted into place with hydraulic jacks.

Fremont Bridge provides 175 feet clearance for tall ships at low water.

The Fremont Bridge is the world's second longest tied arch bridge and the longest bridge structure on the Oregon state highway system.

the Willamette River. As a result, ODOT invited PAC to participate in the design concept for Fremont Bridge, then on the drawing board. Werner Storch, of Storch Engineering, an industrial engineering firm located in Portland at the time, acted as consultant to PAC. Storch, born in Europe, admired a bridge near Vancouver, British Columbia that was a pleasing arch design and solved the boggy site conditions present at Fremont's location. The Port Mann Bridge crosses the Fraser River in a suburb of Vancouver. It opened in 1964, its design inspired by bridges in Europe. (One of the most beautiful steel tied arches in the world is the Passerelle de Billy pedestrian bridge, located beneath the Eiffel Tower and opened in the late 1800s.) Storch's office submitted a rendering of Port Mann to PAC; this concept was then presented by ODOT to its consulting engineering company, Parsons, Brinckerhoff, Quade & Douglas (PBQ&D) of New York City. PBQ&D then designed Fremont to replicate Port Mann's three-span tied arch form, using computers for the first time to help with Fremont's complicated calculations. PBQ&D (now Parsons Brinckerhoff) is an engineering company known for designing transportation systems, including the IRT (1904) in New York and BART (1962) in the San Francisco Bay Area. They also designed Portland's three-mile-long Westside Light Rail tunnel (1998) and the East Side and West Side "Big Pipe" sewer tunnels for Portland's $1 billion Combined Sewer Overflow (CSO) program, the largest construction project in Oregon's history.

Nearly as complicated as Fremont's main tied arch structure, the bridge's gigantic east and west approaches were designed by Howard, Needles, Tammen & Bergendoff (HNTB), of Kansas City, Missouri. HNTB, also nationally known, has designed several Oregon bridges, including the original Interstate Bridge (1917), the replacement lift span for BNSF Railway Bridge 5.1 (1989), and the second Alsea Bay Bridge (1991). The tied arch contractor was Murphy Pacific Corp. of Richmond, California, with Earl and Wright Consulting Engineers as erection consultants. Other major contractors were Peter Kiewit Sons' Co., Andersen-Hannan, and Drake-Willamette.

Unusual Note—Using 2005 National Bridge Inventory data, the Federal Highway Administration estimates that there are 128 steel tied arch bridges in the U.S. (out of about 600,000 public highway bridges), with the Fremont even rarer because it is a three-span tied arch.

Approaches—East end: Main approach (southbound and northbound), I-5. West end: Main approach (southbound and northbound), I-405.

The Fremont was designed and built to help solve inner-city traffic problems. The bridge closed the gap in the interstate freeway system in downtown Portland when it linked the system's westside loop, I-405 (sometimes referred to as the Stadium Freeway), to Marquam Bridge and I-5 on the east bank of the river. The Fremont Bridge also provides easy access from North Portland to the Beaverton area, and from Northeast Portland to Northwest Portland.

Neighborhood/Landmarks—Travelers crossing the Fremont see the upstream cityscape of downtown Portland. Downstream and to the west are Terminal 2, where lumber and steel are loaded and unloaded round-the-clock, and a more industrialized waterfront. However, due to zoning changes, apartment houses and condominiums can now be seen north of Fremont's west end footings. On the eastside, one can see the southern tip of Swan Island and, beyond that, the residence-dotted hillside of Mock's Crest. Under the bridge on the east end is one of the busiest railyards in the country, the Union Pacific's 186-acre Albina yards. First measured for track in 1882, this yard is a landmark with its 160-foot smoke stack, dating to 1885.

BROADWAY BRIDGE

BROADWAY
river mile 11.7

Opened
22 April 1913

Structure Types
Six steel through truss spans with one double-leaf Rall bascule movable main span and five fixed spans; four fixed spans are Pennsylvania-Petit trusses and one is a Pratt truss. Steel plate girder approach spans.

Main Span Length
278 feet

Center Height to Water
90 feet

Outside Width
70 feet (four traffic lanes, with two 11-foot sidewalk/bike paths)

Color
"Golden Gate" red

Cost
$1.6 million
eight-phase rehabilitation 2001-2010,
$40 million (projected)

Owner
Multnomah County, built by City of Portland

Design Engineers
Ralph Modjeski, Chicago;
Strobel Engineering, Chicago (bascule span)

Access
pedestrians, bicycles allowed

Bridge Opening Signals
audible: two long, one short;
radio call sign: (channel 13) KLU 724

Average Daily Traffic
30,000

Historic American Engineering Record
OR-22 and Addendum

THE BROADWAY, the longest double-leaf bascule drawbridge in the world when it opened, is a "rolling" lift span. It has one of the most complicated and rarest opening methods of any movable bridge type anywhere. The distinctive brick-red bridge—matched by nearby Union Station and the riverfront McCormick Pier apartments and condominiums—is located six-tenths of a mile upriver from the Fremont and connects Northwest Portland to Northeast Portland.

The first bascule span in Portland, the opening of the Broadway in 1913 marked a new period of bridge technology. Portland's population had outgrown both the original ferry system and the earlier lightweight bridges. The Broadway was seen as the answer to the problem of heavy traffic between the west side and the rapidly growing east side. Its completion caused a shift

The Broadway Bridge with its bascule in the open position.

in Portland's land values and extended the central business district. The city needed a bridge downriver from the Steel Bridge (at river mile 12.1, the farthest bridge downstream at the time). The opening of the Broadway was also a bridge ownership landmark. A bill passed by the legislature in 1913 took the city of Portland "out of bridge building and maintenance affairs, transferring responsibility for construction, operation, and maintenance ... to Multnomah County."

According to a newspaper account at the time, "The designing engineer said the structure should be able to carry traffic for 100 years."

In 1910, the year before construction of the Broadway began, there were only 2,500 licensed vehicles in Oregon, but by 1913 there were 14,000. Photographs show traffic jams on the Broadway by 1926.

During the time the Broadway was taking shape, news of the completion of Reed College in 1912 and the construction of the Vista House at Crown Point (as part of the Columbia River Highway) came with the announcement of plans for opening the Panama Canal. Another Portland-area bridge—the long-awaited spanning of the Columbia between Portland and

Vancouver—was on the drawing boards. A single-span Interstate would be the next large vehicle bridge in the Portland area, opening in 1917.

Name—The structure takes its name from its main connecting street: Broadway is a name common to many main streets across America. The east side connecting street has always been called Broadway, but the west side street (originally platted in the 1850s as Seventh) was renamed when the bridge opened.

Bridge Statistics—The bridge is composed of one movable and five fixed spans and is one of the world's outstanding examples of the Rall-type bascule span. The Rall span (named for the inventor of its opening mechanism) makes the Broadway unique. The lift span has movable portions made up of steel through (enclosed) trusses, which provide 250 feet of lateral waterway clearance, allowing ocean-going freighters to berth at an upstream grain elevator. Both lift span leaves, each 148.5 feet in length, are hinged about the Rall wheels. The counterweighted leaves glide backward and upward on the eight-foot diameter wheels along steel tracks three feet wide by 32 feet long. The weight supported by each wheel is more than two million pounds; each leaf, with its above-deck counterweight, weighs twice that amount, or 2,000 tons.

The preliminary plans for Broadway were prepared such that bids were invited for four different lift span types: Strauss bascule, Scherzer rolling lift. Strauss modified designs, and Rall bascule. The latter was finally adopted because it was the cheapest, after—according to reports—"a spirited

The Broadway Bridge opened in 1913 with streetcar tracks.

contest by representatives of the other types."
According to an *Engineering News* report of
the day: "Each leaf consists essentially of two
trusses, each supported by a roller and with
a short back arm or tail, so counterweighted
that but small pressure is needed to make the
leaf rotate about the shaft of the roller." Basic
to the entire movement of each leaf are two
trunnions, three feet long and 18 inches in
diameter, the largest axle shafts in the bridge.
Located in the two wheels, one on each side of
the bridge, these trunnions are the mechanisms
around which the workings of the Broadway
pivot. Again, from the report: "The leaf has, at
the same time, a longitudinal movement given
by the travel of the roller on its track, so that
the two movements combined lift the main
arm of the leaf into a nearly vertical position

Broadway's historic lighting and railing.

and at the same time move it back from the channel, so as to secure a great clear width of open channel."

The bridge piers (V and VI) that carry the bascule span sit on caissons 50 feet high, which is different from the other Portland bridges. The concrete pier bodies are overlaid with granite facing. See Unusual Note below.

The bridge opened with a lift span roadway made of Shuman-brand paving (hardwood soaked in tar). It was closed for six months in 1927 for expansion work that placed Port Orford cedar from the Oregon coast on the bridge's lift span, upgraded the fixed-span roadway decks from wood to concrete, and added the Lovejoy Viaduct. At the time of the bridge's construction, electric rail cars were a major form of urban transportation. In 1914, according to the city's "Traffic Survey Summary for Willamette River Bridges," more than seven million passengers rode in streetcars across the Broadway.

In 1948, the bridge's lift span deck was replaced with steel grating. A serious mechanical problem occurred in 1978 when one of the four Rall wheels cracked (see below).

In 1982 the bridge once again accommodated changing traffic patterns. Signals and curb ramps, intended to help move bicycles safely over the bridge to downtown, were installed as part of the Portland Bicycle Route System, at a cost of $18,000. In 2006, more than 2,000 bicyclists cross on a daily basis and TriMet buses make 128 trips (1,100 riders). This is in addition to almost 30,000 vehicle crossings.

In 1999, the 72-year-old Lovejoy Viaduct was razed to make room for the River District, a new neighborhood between Union Station, the Pearl District, and Naito Parkway. Demolition and clean up to remove the Lovejoy Viaduct, which extended between the bridge and N.W. 14th, cost $1 million. It has now been replaced by a shorter Lovejoy Ramp (designed by HNTB Engineering), opened in 2003 at a cost of $10 million. The bridge's streetlights were also replaced in 2001, historically correct sidewalk lights were added to the bridge, and the Broadway Ramp sidewalks were replaced. The Willamette Light Brigade, a private citizens' group, has since commissioned design concepts for permanent decorative lighting for the Burnside, Steel, and Broadway bridges (Morrison and Hawthorne already completed). Engineering plans for

Installation of fiber reinforced polymer (FRP) deck panel on bascule span.

Workers lowering FRP deck panel into place.

Broadway's system are under contract, but additional fundraising is necessary to install the Broadway plan.

In January 2002, the bridge was closed to motor vehicles, bicycles, and pedestrians while four anchor struts were replaced and the operating struts were rehabilitated. (The anchor struts bear the weight of the lift span leaves when the bridge is closed.) The engineers for the replacement/repair of the struts were CH2M Hill and Hardesty & Hanover. Christie was the contractor.

Between February 2003 and April 2005, Multnomah County spent another $26.3 million on additional repairs. This contract called for a new fiber reinforced polymer deck on the lift span, a microsilica concrete overlay on the fixed-span decks, new sidewalks and paint, a new stormwater collection and treatment system, new electric motors, and a new electrical control system. The County and David Evans &

Associates worked with more than 15 regulatory and oversight agencies and business owners throughout the 2003-05 project. The contractor was Mowat, with Abhe & Svoboda and M-Cutter as subcontractors.

Engineers/Builders—The Broadway Bridge was designed and built under the supervision of Ralph Modjeski, of Chicago. The Pennsylvania Steel Co. of Steelton, Pennsylvania, fabricated and erected the superstructure. Union Bridge and Construction Co. of Kansas City built the substructure. The bascule span itself was designed by Strobel Engineering of Chicago. The lift mechanism patent belonged to Theodor Rall.

Polish-born Modjeski (1861-1940) came to live in the United States with his mother, a famous opera singer, when he was 15. He left to study engineering in Paris, and later became internationally famous. He was responsible for the design and construction or the rebuilding

35

Broadway Bridge's shoreline piers are steel-plate pipes filled with concrete.

of 30 of America's major bridges, four of which were record-setters and are considered classics. One of his most famous is the Ben Franklin Bridge (the Philadephia-Camden Bridge, when built), the longest suspension bridge in the world for a time. In Oregon,

Modjeski also designed the Portland to Vancouver railroad bridges completed in 1908-09, now named the BNSF 5.1, 8.8, and 9.6 bridges, as well as the Oregon Trunk Railroad bridge (1911) across central Oregon's Crooked River Canyon.

Unusual Note—The four piers supporting the Broadway Bridge's river spans are founded on concrete-filled wooden caissons of the pneumatic (compressed air) type. Pneumatic caissons were also used on the Brooklyn Bridge (1883) in New York City. More than 80

Broadway Bridge's four river piers sit on pneumatic caissons. The two center piers are faced with granite quarried near Index, Washington.

When bascule span opens, each 2,000-ton leaf rolls and tilts on two 8-foot Rall wheels.

feet deep and located at the west shoreline, Broadway's Pier IV caisson was the deepest pneumatic bridge caisson in the U.S. at the time of its construction in 1913.

Approaches—East end: Broadway. West end: Broadway, Lovejoy Street.

Neighborhood/Landmarks—On Broadway's west end, adjacent to the north side of the bridge, is the historic Albers Mill (1909-11). Broadway Bridge is in the heart of Portland harbor: To the south of the bridge are CLD Pacific Grain Elevators, and to the north, Irving Grain Elevators (last count, the two elevator operations loaded four million tons of wheat onto grain delivering to countries around the world). Openings for grain ships, the Rose Festival fleet, and other river traffic, and nearly as many openings for repairs and maintenance, add up to more than 20 openings a month—a lot of heavy movement for an old and complex riveted truss bridge. While average opening times for Morrison, Burnside and Hawthorne bridges run from five to eight minutes, openings on the Broadway can take 20 minutes and longer.

STEEL BRIDGE

STEEL
river mile 12.1

Opened
mid-July 1912 (trains) 9 August 1912 (other)

Precursor
1888

Structure Types
Three steel double-deck truss spans with one vertical lift movable main span and two fixed side spans; all spans are Pratt trusses. Steel plate girder and reinforced concrete girder approach spans.

Main Span Length
211 feet

Center Height to Water
72 feet (upper deck) 26 feet (lower deck)

Outside Width
71 feet (four traffic lanes with two 6-foot sidewalks)

Color
gun-metal black

Cost
$1.7 million plus $10 million for MAX redesign and bridge rehabilitation (1984-86) and $2.5 million for RiverWalk (2001)

Owner
Union Pacific Railroad

Design Engineers
Waddell & Harrington, Kansas City, Missouri

Access
pedestrians, bicycles allowed on highway deck; since 2001, on railroad deck

Bridge Opening Signals
audible: one long, one short
radio call sign: (channel 13) KQU 534

Average Daily Traffic
23,000

Historic American Engineering Record
OR-21 and Addendum

STEEL BRIDGE—dominating the river skyline at river mile 12.1—is the only double-deck vertical lift bridge of its type in the world. Built by Oregon-Washington Railway & Navigation Co. (OWR&N), the lower deck of the lift span (built for trains) may be lifted independently, telescoping into trusses of the upper deck (built for street railways, pedestrians, and gasoline- and horse-powered vehicles), or both decks may be lifted together. When Steel Bridge's lower deck is raised, canoes and other small river craft can pass without requiring the operator to raise the entire bridge. Metropolitan Area Express (MAX) light rail was added to the highway deck in 1986, linking MAX from downtown Portland 16 miles east to Gresham. In 1988, service opened to Hillsboro and, in 2001, when Steel was 89 years old, to Portland International Airport. Also in 2001, RiverWalk opened across Steel's bottom deck, a $2.5 million

The 1888 Steel Bridge was a double-deck swing span.

Both decks on the Steel Bridge lifted, with Burnside Bridge bascule leaf and railing in foreground.

cantilevered pedestrian and bicycle walkway linking the northern terminus of Tom McCall Park to the northern terminus of Vera Katz Eastbank Esplanade. Today's average daily traffic count across the top deck is 23,100 vehicles. Add 772 TriMet bus trips (13,000 riders), and 482 MAX crossings (31,000 riders), plus several hundred pedestrians and bicyclists who use both the upper sidewalks and the bottom deck's RiverWalk, and multimodal, a word introduced into the English language in 1899, seems to have been invented anticipating the Steel Bridge.

With only 26 feet clearance at low water level, major floods in 1948, 1964, and 1996 threatened the bridge's bottom deck. The year the second Steel opened, Maria Montessori started her school, Peninsula Park and Ladd's Circle were planted with roses, Lents was annexed to Portland, and Simon Benson donated money to install four-bowl drinking fountains downtown. Another riveted structure, the *Titanic*, failed just three months before Steel opened for business in July 1912. The following year, Broadway Bridge opened on the Willamette and four years later, Interstate Bridge on the Columbia connected Portland to Vancouver—two other truss bridges also held together by rivets.

Name—When the predecessor to today's Steel opened in 1888 (19 years after the "Golden Spike" was driven at Promontory, Utah, celebrating the first transcontinental railroad), it caused a stir. Wrought iron and wood were the readily available material for bridges of the day, but the first railroad bridge across the Willamette at Portland was made of steel (see glossary). That adjective soon became the common name for the structure.

Steel's lower deck lifts independently, telescoping into the trusses of the upper deck.

At a point just downstream from today's bridge, the 1888 Steel was also a double-decker, but the movable portion was a swing span. Local usage kept the descriptive name alive for the 1912 bridge.

Bridge Statistics—This imposing structure is so large that OWR&N and the construction company had to develop innovative techniques in order to build it. Steel Bridge's main span is a 211-foot steel through double-deck vertical lift truss flanked by two steel through truss approach spans. Dual cable systems and independent counterweights located in the bridge's towers are integral to operation of both lift spans. Each deck has its own set of counterweights: the upper deck has two, one on each end; the lower deck has a total of eight, four on each end. The total moving load, upper and lower decks and counterweights, is roughly nine million pounds. The machinery house is located on top of the top deck, mid-span between the towers. The Steel Bridge operator's room is suspended under this house, so that the operator (employed by Union Pacific) can observe the main deck as well as river traffic. The highway deck is under the supervision of ODOT, with a crew room located at the west end of the bridge. Six gate tenders are available (on-call) to operate the highway traffic gates during any top deck lifts. In 1914, Steel's lower deck raised 20,399 times. By 1943, the lower deck raised only 10,687 times annually. The decline continues.

Engineers/Builders—The firm of Waddell & Harrington, consulting engineers, Kansas City, Missouri, designed Steel Bridge, with credit for the double-deck engineering technology going to John Lyle Harrington (1868-1942). (For more about John Alexander Low Waddell, see Hawthorne Bridge and the glossary.) The lift span was invented and patented by Waddell and Harrington. The design fee and supervision included the patent royalty. The engineering department of OWR&N supervised erection of the superstructure. Robert Wakefield & Co. of Portland was the contractor. The substructure contract was awarded to Union Bridge and Construction Co., also from Kansas City.

The bridge's major rehabilitation and MAX construction in 1986 was designed by ODOT, with HNTB working with Union Pacific Railroad on change-out of the bridge's steel counterweight lifting ropes. HNTB also designed Steel's RiverWalk (see Hawthorne Bridge and Bridge 5.1).

Unusual Note—Steel Bridge is the second oldest vertical lift bridge in North America (Hawthorne the oldest) and a classic example of early

Steel Bridge lift span machinery.

The Steel Bridge is the only double-deck vertical lift bridge of its type in the world. Its lower deck can be lifted with or without raising the top deck.

20th century mechanical engineering. Other vertical lift bridges in the Northwest designed by Waddell & Harrington (or successor firms) include Hawthorne Bridge (1910); Interstate Bridge (1917); and Tacoma, Washington's Murray Morgan Bridge, built as City Waterway Bridge (1913). Houghton-Hancock Bridge (1959), a 263-foot double-deck vertical lift span over the Portage Lake Ship Canal in Michigan, also has an upper highway and a lower railway deck, and at one time, Carlton Bridge in Bath, Maine, a 234-foot double-deck vertical lift, carried rail on its bottom deck and traffic on its upper, but its highway deck was removed a few years ago. In any event, neither of these bridges, nor any other, has ever been capable of the independent deck movement unique to the Steel Bridge.

Approaches—East end: Holladay Street, Interstate Avenue. West end: Everett Street, Glisan Street, Naito Parkway.

Neighborhood/Landmarks—At Steel Bridge's east end are twin spires of the Oregon Convention Center, the Rose Quarter, and track for Interstate MAX light rail. To the west are the old Bekins Storage Building, ODOT's Region One headquarters, Port of Portland offices, and the Portland Classical Chinese Garden. The garden leads to New Chinatown/Japantown, a National Historic District, with red lampposts, festival sidewalks, and new cherry trees, planted in 2006.

BURNSIDE BRIDGE

BURNSIDE
river mile 12.4

Opened
28 May 1926

Precursor
1894

Structure Types
Three steel deck truss spans with one double-leaf
Strauss bascule movable main span and two fixed
side spans; side spans are double-intersection Warren
trusses with sub-verticals. Reinforced concrete
girder and steel plate girder approach spans.

Main Span Length
252 feet Center

Height to Water
64 feet

Outside Width
86 feet (five traffic lanes and two bicycle lanes,
with two 7-foot sidewalks)

Color
yellow ochre; towers: red, beige, and green

Cost
$3 million; three-phase rehabilitation 2002-2007,
$12.3 million

Owner
Multnomah County

Design Engineers
Hedrick & Kremers, Portland; Gustav Lindenthal,
New York; Joseph Strauss, Chicago (bascule)

Access
pedestrians, bicycles allowed

Bridge Opening Signals
audible: one long, two short;
radio call sign: (channel 13) KTD 520

Average Daily Traffic
40,000

Historic American Engineering Record
OR-101

A S THE ROAR OF THE 1920S promised everlasting prosperity, the din of bridge
building could be heard up and down the Willamette's waterfront. In that decade, voters
approved a $4.5 million bond issue for building two fixed-span bridges (see Ross Island
and Sellwood bridges) and to replace the slow-opening swing-span Burnside Bridge, opened in
1894. Upstream, at river mile 25.9, Oregon City was getting a new arch bridge; downstream, the
1913 Broadway Bridge was being renovated and the first Lovejoy Viaduct added. However, just
as the era was spiked with illegal spirits, so were some of the area's politicians spiked for illegal
activities. Taxpayers learned the Burnside's construction contract was let for a half a million
dollars more than the lowest bid. The discovered malfeasance resulted in criminal indictments.
Three county commissioners were recalled when they, along with the consulting bridge engineers,
were caught in a million-dollar scheme involving Portland's three Roaring Twenties bridges.
Newly-appointed Multnomah County commissioners went to work quickly and awarded the
Burnside Bridge contract to Pacific Bridge Co. and hired Gustav Lindenthal, a famous New York
City bridge engineer, to take over Burnside's design and construction.

The 1894 Burnside Bridge was a slow-opening swing span.

Bascule span lift machinery in machinery house.

When it opened 28 May 1926, *The Oregonian* commented: "The completion of the Burnside, Sellwood and Ross Island bridges marks very definitely the arrival of the motor and machine age in Portland with its accompanying problems in the movement of swiftly impelled vehicles." The city was 180 times larger than it had been when Burnside Street was platted. Portland's population had surpassed 250,000, and land had been annexed to expand the city limits to more than 66 square miles.

Name—Before 1891, Burnside Street was simply "B" Street in the order of alphabetically designated streets in Northwest Portland. That year it was renamed to honor Vermont native Dan Wyman Burnside (1825-1887), listed in the 1878 Portland City Directory as "agent Imperial Flouring Mills" on Front Avenue (now Naito Parkway). Burnside also served on the committee charged with raising private funds (no public money then available) that launched the Corps of Engineers on a 17-foot Willamette River channel dredging project in 1866. He and his partner, Thomas A. Savier, donated $300 to the cause. Burnside is buried in Section 3, Lot 8 of River View Cemetery in Southwest Portland.

Bridge Statistics—Burnside Bridge, like Morrison and Broadway bridges, is a double-leaf bascule span, which means the roadway decks lift up from their ends, much like opposing flaps of a cardboard box. In such movable bridges, the lift spans are counterbalanced by concrete weights. These weights are located, one each, inside Burnside's two river piers. (This is also true of Morrison and Broadway bridges, but on Broadway, the counterweights are located above deck, rather than below.) When

Burnside Bridge bascule span construction, ca. 1925. Pier walls were built after the bascule leaves and counterweights.

Burnside Bridge's 252-foot center span divides, the two leaves—each 126 feet long—swing up to allow about 200 feet of horizontal clearance for river traffic. While the lifting decks on Morrison are open steel grating and Broadway's a lightweight polymer, Burnside's deck is solid concrete, requiring a 1,900-ton counterweight in each pier to lift the deck. Burnside's lift span weighs 5,000 tons—nearly twice as much as Morrison's—and is one of the heaviest bascule highway bridges in the U.S. The Burnside Bridge is reportedly the first major bascule span in the U.S. built with

an all-concrete deck. Pile "clusters" support Burnside's river piers. The clusters are made of 40-foot-tall Douglas fir tree trunks. Each bascule pier is supported by 380 tree trunks, much like an underwater pin cushion.

Burnside can be operated only from the west tower, located on the south side of the span, and is attended full-time only during high water. Requests to open the draw during low water must be directed to the Hawthorne Bridge operator, on-duty 24 hours a day. The Hawthorne operator also coordinates

the activities of the 16 full-time and part-time ("on-call") bridge operators employed by Multnomah County in 2006. Bridge operators belong to Local 88 of the American Federation of State, County, and Municipal Employees. The Burnside opened 425 times in 2006, for an average of 35 openings a month. It carried 45,000 vehicles and 420 TriMet bus trips (7,900 riders) each day. In 1995, one of six traffic lanes on the bridge was removed to accommodate bicycle lanes. There were 620 bicycle crossings a day in 1995, with nearly 1,200 crossings a day in 2006.

Steel girders for Burnside Bridge approach spans inspected by engineer Kurt Siecke, ca. 1925.

River view of bascule leaf.

The ornate towers were designed by architects Houghtaling and Dougan.

In the mid-1990s, Burnside Street was declared a Regional Emergency Transportation Route with Burnside the one non-freeway span for public agencies to route emergency vehicles, equipment, and supplies across the Willamette River in case of earthquake or other disasters. In 2002, Burnside Bridge's approaches were given a new driving surface, a cleaner stormwater drainage system was added, and the bridge was seismically retrofitted—making it the first bridge maintained by Multnomah County to be protected against earthquake. Phase 1 seismic upgrade added steel connections between deck sections and piers. (Still vulnerable are the bridge's counterweight-heavy piers and its east-end horizontal steel girders, encased in concrete during construction to protect them from fire. For more about earthquake, see Bridge 101 and the Rivers.) David Evans & Associates designed the $2.1 million approach deck and seismic upgrade. The contractor was Mowat. In 2003, in a $1.2 million project, Heil Electric replaced outdated wiring causing operational malfunctions on both the Burnside and Morrison bridges. They removed seven tons of old equipment on Burnside alone and installed touch control screens

Burnside tower with harbor wall and downtown Portland in background.

in the operator's tower. (Both Morrison and Burnside can now be controlled from a remote site.) In a two-year lift span rehabilitation project scheduled to be completed by the end of 2007, the rundown 80-year-old concrete deck on Burnside's lift span is being removed and replaced. As part of this $9 million contract, mechanical parts that help open the bridge are also being replaced. One of the hinges attaching the 3.5-million pound counterweight to the east lift span leaf is worn out and cannot turn freely. The frozen hinge causes the east leaf to open slower than the west leaf. OBEC Consulting Engineers designed the repairs, with assistance from mechanical engineering consultants Hardesty & Hanover. The contractor is Advanced American Construction. In addition, the Willamette Light Brigade, a private citizens' group, has commissioned design concepts for permanent architectural lighting for the Burnside, Steel, and Broadway bridges (Morrison and Hawthorne already completed). Engineering plans for Burnside's system are under contract, but additional fundraising is necessary to install the Burnside plan.

Engineers/Builders—Designers were Ira G. Hedrick, a former partner with John Waddell (designer of the Hawthorne, Steel, and Interstate bridges) and Robert Kremers. Gustav Lindenthal, of New York, served as the consulting engineer. Lindenthal was hired to complete the design and supervise the bridge's entire construction. The double-leaf Strauss bascule system was developed by Joseph B. Strauss (1870-1938), who, with Charles Ellis, was responsible for San Francisco's Golden Gate Bridge (1937). Prime contractors were Pacific Bridge (main span), Lindstrom & Feigenson (approach

The solid concrete deck on the Burnside Bridge's bascule span is balanced by massive 1,900-ton concrete counterweights inside the two river piers.

end ramps), and NePage McKenny (lighting). Subcontractors included Lindstrom & Feigenson, Booth & Pomeroy, and Jaggar Sroufe.

Lindenthal (1850-1935) was born in Brunn (Brno), Czechoslovakia (now Czech Republic). Commissioner of Bridges in New York City in 1901-1902, he was known as the dean of American bridge engineers. Among his important contributions are the Queensboro Bridge (1909) and Hell Gate arch (1917) in New York City, and the Smithfield lenticular truss bridge (1883) in Pittsburgh. Burnside's distinctive Italian Renaissance towers reflect the early 20th century City Beautiful Movement that called for adding architectural ornamentation to engineering designs. Houghtaling and Dougan of Portland were the architects.

Unusual Note—When the 1894 Burnside was dismantled in 1925, its 300-foot east fixed truss was placed across the Sandy River at Dodge Park, and the 240-foot west truss across the Bull Run River near Roslyn Lake. Both of these bridges still serve in Clackamas County, evidence of early recycling efforts. For more about Burnside's old parts, see *Historic Highway Bridges of Oregon*. The 1894 approach span girders are also being used, one pair at each end of the Sellwood Bridge, opened in 1925.

Approaches—East end: Burnside Street, pedestrian stairs to Eastbank Esplanade. West end: Burnside Street.

Neighborhood/Landmarks—As most residents know and visitors soon learn, the Willamette River separates Portland east from west and the Burnside Bridge separates north from south. A fifth section, that area known as North Portland, incorporates St. Johns and other neighborhoods and industrial sections in "the Peninsula." At the west end of Burnside Bridge is the three-bay, five-roof Chinese Gate (1986), and the neon "Old Town" sign, noting the historic Skidmore/Old Town District, located on both sides of West Burnside Street. Also under the west end is the harbor wall (1929). In 1994-95, stairs to Naito Parkway were razed, with new stairs and "Welcome to Saturday Market" signs erected on the north and south sides of the west end. (The open-air Saturday Market operates on weekends, March through December, with plans afoot to move it to a nearby location after 2008.) Under the bridge's east end is a nationally famous public skateboard ramp designed and built by its youthful users. Each June the Rose Festival Grand Floral Parade closes Burnside for a few hours while marchers and flowered floats cross east to west. The best views of the Burnside's understructure can be seen from the Ankeny Street Dock in Tom McCall Waterfront Park or from the Vera Katz Eastbank Esplanade. Since the completion of the Eastbank Esplanade and a stairway from the Burnside's southeast end in 2001, walkers and bicyclists have direct access to the east bank of the Willamette River.

MORRISON BRIDGE

MORRISON
river mile 12.8

Opened
24 May 1958

Precursors
1887, 1905

Structure Types
Three steel deck truss spans with one double-leaf Chicago-style (fixed trunnion) bascule movable main span and two fixed side spans; side spans are Pratt trusses with curved bottom chords. Steel plate girder approach spans.

Main Span Length
284 feet

Center Height to Water
69 feet

Outside Width
78 feet (six traffic lanes, with two 5-foot sidewalks)

Color
"aluminum" gray

Cost
$12.9 million

Owner
Multnomah County

Design Engineers
Sverdrup & Parcel, St. Louis;
Moffatt, Nichol & Taylor, Portland

Access
pedestrians, bicycles allowed

Bridge Opening Signals
audible: one long, three short;
radio call sign: (channel 13) KTD 522

Average Daily Traffic
50,000

Historic American Engineering Record
OR-100

NO EXPENSE WAS SPARED for opening-day festivities when the Morrison Bridge opened on 24 May 1958. Mayor Terry Schrunk dedicated the bridge in a formal ceremony. The Benson and Wilson high school bands, escorted by Air Force and Marine color guards, marched from each end of the span toward the center. Coursing up the river, fireboats aimed pressure-shot water into the air as delta-winged F-102 jets flew overhead.

The current design is the third bridge at river mile 12.8. Both of the previous structures (1887 and 1905) were swing spans, with the 1887 structure the first bridge across the lower Willamette River in Portland. It was a toll bridge. Rates were as follows: for two horses and one driver, 20 cents; one

The 1887 Morrison Bridge, the first bridge across the lower Willamette River.

The second Morrison Bridge (1905) carried streetcars.

horse and driver, 15 cents; one horse and rider, 10 cents; footmen, 5 cents; loose horses and cattle, 10 cents each; loose sheep and hogs, 5 cents each. A sign over mid-span admonished: "Walk Your Horses on the Draw." After the spate of bridge building in the 1920s and opening of the St. Johns Bridge in 1931, other more pressing concerns during the Depression and the Second World War prevented the construction of any trans-Willamette bridges for more than 25 years with the exception of the Sauvie Island Bridge, opened across the Multnomah Channel of the Willamette River in 1950.

The new 1958 Morrison Bridge opened none too soon for the city's daily commuters. Swinging open for river traffic up to 500 times a month and gear malfunctions caused by hot summer weather rendered the pre-automobile Morrison obsolete long before it was replaced. (The flood that destroyed the nearby city of Vanport in 1948 trespassed into Portland's eastside, closing the half-century-old Morrison Bridge for a month.)

Nationally, in 1958 the New York Giants and Brooklyn Dodgers moved to California. First-class postage went from three to four cents. *Doctor Zhivago* was published, and hula hoops were invented. On the Columbia River, world-famous Celilo Falls had been silent one year under the newly formed lake behind The Dalles Dam about the time *Sputnik*, the first satellite, began orbiting the earth. Morrison's large concrete and steel (pile) foundations, open-grating steel deck, and air traffic control-style towers reflect a minimalist, space-age architecture and an era when many airports were being built. When the bridge turns 50 in May 2008, it becomes eligible for the National Register of Historic Places.

1958 Morrison Bridge under construction next to 1905 Morrison.

Name—The Morrison takes its name from the street it serves. John L. Morrison (1819-99) earned the name "The Godfather of Morrison Street" because he built the first house on what is now a main thoroughfare extending east and west across the Willamette River. A carpenter while he lived in Portland, this 1831 Scottish émigré was also one of the original 51 men who voted "yes" at Champoeg in 1843 to establish Oregon's provisional government. Never married, Morrison is buried in Lot 123 in the Valley Church Cemetery (formerly the Valley Presbyterian Cemetery) in Friday Harbor, San Juan County, Washington.

Bridge Statistics—The Morrison is a three-span steel structure consisting of two deck truss spans and a double-leaf Chicago-style trunnion bascule. The movable span, which takes approximately eight minutes to open and close, allows clearance of 220 feet between the bascule piers. Each leaf is 150 feet long and is opened by a counterweight weighing 950 tons. The counterweights are located behind pivot points inside the two main river piers and are propelled by rack and pinion systems and gears 36 feet tall operated by 100-horsepower electrical motors. The open-ended piers, visible only from the downstream side, minimize the piling up of water as the river passes, reducing

turbulence for navigators. Both of Morrison's towers are located on the south side of the bridge, one on each side of the river's main channel. However, the bridge is operated from the west end tower only. In 2005, the Morrison opened 400 times, or a little more than 30 times a month. It is one of the County's "on-call" bridges—meaning during low water periods, river users must make an appointment for a lift. At the intersection of two interstate freeways, Morrison serves as a major travel link—it carried about 50,000 vehicles a day at the end of 2000. Metro predicts 25 percent more traffic by 2015.

The steel grating deck on Morrison's bascule span is scheduled for replacement in the near future. The surface, worn smooth after a half-century of high-speed traffic and heavier and heavier use, is proving especially slick in wet weather. In May 2004, 39-year-old Lynda Pilger was struck and killed while walking her dog on the southeast side of the bridge during a rainstorm. A driver traveling eastbound on the bridge in a SUV lost control on the metal grating and jumped the sidewalk. In another rainy day incident, in March 2005, a driver lost control of her Isuzu Rodeo on the grating, slammed through a guardrail, and plunged 60 feet off the northwest side of the bridge to the bottom of the Willamette River. A Portland Fire Bureau diver rescued her after she freed herself and made it to the surface. Making traffic rules on the bridge more visible, in 2005 Multnomah County installed new signs and painted new lane stripes on the metal grating and approaches. They warn drivers it is illegal to change lanes or speed while crossing on the grating in either direction. During a closure of the Hawthorne Bridge in 1998-99, a temporary bicycle/pedestrian path was installed across

Tail end of Morrison Bridge bascule leaf during an opening.

Morrison to reroute foot and bike traffic. More than 450 residents sent postcards to the County asking that the Morrison Bridge path be preserved. An engineering study has since been done and a permanent bike and pedestrian facility is in the works. In 2001, the east end ramps on the bridge were refurbished with a new microsilica concrete overlay at a cost of $3.1 million. Multnomah County performed the engineering and Wildish Standard Paving was the contractor. In 2003, Heil Electric replaced outdated wiring causing operational malfunctions on both the Burnside and Morrison bridges. Morrison Bridge's traffic gates were replaced and its old submarine cables were taken out of service. The east end machinery is now controlled by radio from the west operator's tower. As part of the $1.2 million rehabilitation, computerized touch screens were installed in the operator towers and 15,000 feet of fiber optic cable laid under the Eastbank Esplanade to connect both bridges to the Multnomah County Bridge Office. This makes it possible for Morrison and Burnside to be opened and closed off-site, if necessary. Morrison's most pressing need is seismic retrofit, due to its design, which includes tall, slim piers. In addition, the bridge is vulnerable because concrete girders rather than steel beams support the bascule (movable) span. Multnomah County estimates major repair projects for

Morrison's towers resemble 1950s-era airport control towers.

The Morrison Bridge bascule span in open position.

Morrison through 2020, including the seismic upgrade, would cost about $50 million.

Engineers/Builders—In 1954, Sverdrup & Parcel, St. Louis, Missouri, and Moffatt, Nichol &Taylor, Inc., Portland, won the engineering contract for the Morrison Bridge. Leif Sverdrup (1898-1976) served under General Douglas MacArthur as chief of airfield construction in the Pacific during World War II, earning the rank of major general. The company also designed the Glenn Jackson I-205 Bridge between Oregon and Washington, the Vandenburg missile launch facility in Southern California, and the 17-mile Chesapeake Bay Bridge-Tunnel in Norfolk, Virginia. Started

in 1928, the company eventually employed more than 21,000 people in 50 U.S. and foreign offices. It was purchased by Jacobs Engineering, an even larger engineering firm, in 1999. The Moffatt firm, established in 1946 (now Moffatt, Nichol & Bonney Architects and Engineers), also designed the Abernethy Bridge at West Linn for ODOT, did the structural and civil design of Portland's Memorial Coliseum (1960), and subconsulting work for design of the Portland Hilton Hotel (1963) and Georgia Pacific (1970) buildings. The contract for Morrison's superstructure, including the bascule span, was awarded to the American Bridge Division of the United States Steel Co., Pittsburgh. The two deck truss

spans were built on barges upriver at the Zidell docks and floated downstream for placement. The bascule span was built in place. The substructure contract was awarded to Manson Construction and Engineering, Seattle. On 22 October 1956, an earthslide killed William Davies, age 53. An ironworker with Local 29, Davies was working on one of the west approach piers. His death reminds us of the dangers of bridge construction.

Unusual Note—Morrison Bridge was the first bridge lighted by the Willamette Light Brigade, a private citizens' group working to light all the downtown river bridges so they do not disappear into the night. Sixteen 1000-watt floodlights with changeable theatrical gel filters to splash color on the bridge's four massive river piers (four lamps per pier, per side) were installed in 1987. WLB is implementing a more-energy efficient system: Thirty-two light-emitting diode (LED) fixtures will replace the 16 floodlights and cut energy use by nearly 84 percent and permit computerized color changes. PacificCorp is donating the final funds for Morrison's upgrade.

Approaches—East end: Grand Avenue, Martin Luther King, Jr. Boulevard, Morrison Street, Belmont Street, Water Avenue, and I-5. West end: Alder Street, Naito Parkway, Washington Street, Second Avenue.

Morrison Bridge does not connect with Morrison Street on the west side. A blank spot on the west side harbor wall provides clues why. This lighter concrete—just south of the existing Morrison Bridge—marks where the second Morrison crossed the wall at Morrison Street between 1905 and 1958. The 1905 swing span was left in place until the extant bridge opened. The new bascule bridge's west end was affixed farther downstream. Keeping up with changing community needs has been a challenge. Multnomah County has modified some of Morrison's original ten on and off approaches to make it a more efficient freeway connector, yet still accessible for pedestrians, bicyclists, and local traffic. When it opened in 1958, there was no I-5 Eastbank Freeway (opened in 1966). On its east end, a circle ramp connects directly to the Eastbank Esplanade.

Neighborhood/Landmarks—Crossing the Morrison Bridge from east to west gives an

Underside of the Morrison Bridge.

The Morrison Bridge looking northeast.

unobstructed view of the city, and offers direct access to the shopping and hotel district. Near the bridge's east end approach is the historic Weatherly Building, Multnomah County offices, and the Central Eastside Industrial District. Travelers on the bridge can also connect with I-5 northbound, or head east on I-84, toward the Columbia River Gorge and Portland International Airport. Following the Water Avenue off-ramp leads to clarklewis, located on a 1910 loading dock and named Portland's restaurant of the year in 2004 by *The Oregonian*.

HAWTHORNE BRIDGE

HAWTHORNE
river mile 13.1

Opened
19 December 1910

Precursors
1891, 1900

Structure Types
Six steel through truss spans with one vertical lift movable span and five fixed spans; all spans are Parker trusses. Steel plate girder and prestressed concrete girder approach spans.

Main Span Length
244 feet

Center Height to Water
49 feet

Vertical Lift
110 feet

Horizontal Clearance
230 feet

Outside Width
73 feet (four traffic lanes, with two 10-foot sidewalks)

Color
green with red trim

Cost
$500,000; $21 million for 1998-99 rehabilitation

Owner
Multnomah County

Design Engineers
Waddell & Harrington, Kansas City, Missouri

Access
pedestrians, bicycles allowed

Bridge Opening Signals
audible: one long, four short
radio call sign: (channel 13) KTD 521

Average Daily Traffic
30,000

Historic American Engineering Record
OR-20 and Addendum

ONE OF THE LOVELIEST VIEWS of west Portland is the intimate prospect across the Willamette from the east end of the Hawthorne—remarkably different from the dramatic vista afforded by the Marquam Bridge, just to the south (upstream). During low water, the accessible Hawthorne Bridge is only 49 feet above the river; often much less during spring runoff.

The vertical lift bridge gained wide popularity across the United States, largely through the efforts of John Alexander Low Waddell (1854-1938), who independently invented and successfully introduced the large-scale high-clearance vertical lift bridge in Chicago. The Hawthorne Bridge is a distinctive and particularly well-preserved example of this early-20th-century American bridge-

Hawthorne Bridge during construction of Harbor Drive, ca. 1942.

the bicycle hub at N.E. Interstate Avenue and N.E. Oregon Street by the Rose Quarter Bus Transit Center, bicyclists can come from just about anywhere on the east side of the river and make a loop using Tom McCall Park on the west side and the Esplanade on the east.

Because Hawthorne's lift span rises an average of 120 times a month—more during the summer because of sailboats—it is also the most opened highway bridge on the Willamette for river traffic. Because of its age, ships or no ships, Hawthorne is opened every eight hours—the revolution of the large sheaves (grooved wheels/pulleys) at the top of the towers keeps the sheave bearings greased. Hawthorne Bridge replaced Madison Bridge No. 2 (1900), which had replaced Madison Bridge No. 1 (1891) after a fire. Due to its propensity for freak accidents, Hawthorne Bridge has been called "the bad luck bridge," but its longevity is proving otherwise.

building technology. It was one of the first vertical lift bridges built and is now the oldest of its kind surviving in the United States. Hawthorne opened in 1910, three years before Portland would get its first traffic light at S.W. Fifth and Washington. This was the year the first electric washing machine was patented and the first airplane took off west of the Rockies. In Portland, the Oregon-Washington Railroad & Navigation Co. was getting ready to build a second Steel Bridge.

All of Portland's early movable bridges had wooden or concrete decks, but Hawthorne's wooden deck was the first to be replaced with a steel roadway deck, not installed until 1945. This deck lasted until 1998, when it was replaced with a second steel deck, also open grating. Such decks are lighter than concrete and allow the rain to fall through. They also "sing," caused by high-speed vibration from vehicle tires against the grating. At the beginning of the 21st century, about 30,000 vehicles cross the bridge every day. Of these, 800 are TriMet buses (17,400 riders), making it, after the Steel Bridge, the second busiest public transit bridge in the state. Hawthorne is also the busiest bicycle-pedestrian bridge in Oregon—last count almost 5,000 bicycle crossings a day. Since the Vera Katz Eastbank Esplanade was finished in 2001 between the Steel and Hawthorne bridges, connecting with

Containment for removal of old lead paint, 1998.

Hawthorne Bridge lift tower, trusses, and roadway deck.

Detail of the truss work.

Hawthorne's railings were designed to keep horses from jumping over the side.

Name—In 1859, Dr. J. C. Hawthorne (1819-81) moved to Oregon and helped found the Oregon Hospital for the Insane, which was located on Asylum Street in East Portland. The street was renamed Hawthorne in 1888, five years after the hospital was moved to Salem. Dr. Hawthorne was one of the first advocates for the 1887 Morrison Bridge across the Willamette. He is buried in Lone Fir Cemetery in Southeast Portland, Block 8M, Lot 44, Grave One North. His monument is one of the largest in Lone Fir.

Bridge Statistics—The main structure of the Hawthorne Bridge is a single-deck, steel through (enclosed) Parker-type truss drawbridge, consisting of five fixed spans and one 244-foot-long lift span resting on seven concrete piers. The length of the bridge proper is 1,382 feet. There is a 20-foot roadway within the enclosed trusses (two ten-foot lanes), a 12-foot lane on either side of the truss structure, and two ten-foot sidewalks. A small wood-frame structure that houses the machinery sits atop the main span. At each end of the lift span there are 165-foot steel-frame towers, each suspending an 880,000-pound reinforced concrete counterweight from 24 one-and-a-half-inch cables. The remaining five secondary fixed spans are each about 200 feet long. Lift bridges such as the Hawthorne fight extra hard against gravity due to the added weight and movement of machinery and counterweights. Steel or iron bridges were first connected with pins, then with rivets, and by the turn of the millennium, with high-strength bolts. There are an estimated half million rivets holding the Hawthorne Bridge together. Most of these were installed in the fabrication shop, probably by machine. The field construction required organized four-man riveting gangs.

Replacing steel grating deck on bridge, 1998.

Designer plaque on the Hawthorne Bridge.

Hawthorne Bridge—view of the deck from underneath.

64

The Hawthorne Bridge leads into the downtown business district.

Hawthorne was repainted with lead-based paint in the 1960s. Bridges are exposed to many harsh elements, with starlings and pigeons among the worst threats in Portland, not counting traffic. Bird droppings, when mixed with rain, create an acid that corrodes steel. In 1985 Hawthorne's eight lift span sheaves (each nine feet in diameter) were replaced. Later, the bridge was fitted for new traffic gate barriers and other safety features, including streetlights. In 1998, the bridge was closed for one year for a $21 million rehabilitation. David Evans & Associates (structural) and Modjeski & Masters (mechanical) were the engineers for this latest project, with Abhe & Svoboda of Minnesota the prime contractor for work that included repainting, new deck, wider sidewalks, lift rope replacement, more mechanical and electrical renovation, and historic restoration of the machinery house. The red and green color scheme was chosen with the help of a citizen committee and the Regional Arts

& Culture Council. Hawthorne, first lighted for the 1912 Rose Festival, was again equipped with architectural lights for the June 1989 Rose Festival through the efforts of the Willamette Light Brigade. This citizens' group works to illuminate Portland's Willamette River bridges so the bridges do not disappear into the night. A permanent design for Hawthorne was installed in 2005 when Portland General Electric and others donated funds for white floodlights to illuminate the operator's house on the lift span, bridge towers, and counterweights.

Hawthorne Bridge lift machinery in machinery house.

Hawthorne Bridge as seen from Tom McCall Waterfront Park.

Engineers/Builders—John Alexander Low Waddell's career as a bridge designer spanned nearly half a century. Considered a pioneer in the use of nickel steel in heavily stressed bridge members, Waddell is best known for his role in developing the vertical lift bridge. His Halsted Street Bridge was built in 1894 in Chicago. In 1910 (the same year the Hawthorne was erected), Waddell built his second lift bridge, this one over the Mississippi River at Keithsburg, Illinois; it had a 234-foot lift span. The Halsted Street Bridge was replaced in 1936, and when the Keithsburg—a single-track Minnesota and St. Louis Railway bridge—caught fire and collapsed 29 June 1981, the Hawthorne assumed the distinction of being the oldest operating vertical lift span in the United States. In addition to his Portland-area structures (see Steel and Interstate bridges), Waddell also designed or supervised the construction of numerous bridges elsewhere in the United States and in Canada, Mexico, Russia, China, Japan, and New Zealand. He worked out of offices in Kansas City, Missouri and New York City. He died at age 84.

The firm of Waddell and Harrington, founded by Waddell in 1887, is the predecessor firm of today's Hardesty & Hanover, New York City; Howard, Needles, Tammen & Bergendoff (HNTB), Kansas City, Missouri; and Harrington & Cortelyou Engineering, Kansas City and Springfield, Missouri. The principal contractor for the Hawthorne Bridge superstructure and approaches was United Engineering & Construction Co., Portland. Robert Wakefield & Co., Portland, was the substructure contractor. Pennsylvania Steel Co. fabricated the steel.

Unusual Note—While in Tom McCall Waterfront Park, walkers can walk on dry land around a pier of the Hawthorne Bridge that was once submerged in the Willamette River. The McCall pier, listed on engineering drawings as Pier VII, stood in the Willamette River until the Portland Harbor Wall opened (1929) and the west side waterfront was filled with dredged material.

Approaches—East end: Grand Ave., Martin Luther King, Jr. Blvd., Madison Street, Hawthorne Blvd. West end: Madison Street, Main Street, Naito Parkway. Bridges are measured by their main span, but if there were an award for number of new approaches, Hawthorne might win as the Portland bridge that has adapted most to survive into the 21st century. Its on- and off-ramps have been rebuilt and reconfigured many times, including its eastern approaches in 1955 and its west approaches in 1957, designed by Moffatt, Nichol & Taylor, Inc., Portland (see Morrison Bridge), and in 1992, when CH2M Hill Engineering designed a replacement for Hawthorne's east-end timber approach section. The replacement is a state-of-the-art earthquake-proof "transition structure" made of prestressed reinforced concrete.

Neighborhood/Landmarks—Every day from the Hawthorne's west end, rain or shine, hundreds of pedestrians and bicyclists exit directly into Tom McCall Waterfront Park, a 23-acre stretch that parallels the Willamette. The park begins at the Steel Bridge and passes under the Burnside, Morrison, and Hawthorne bridges. It was extended when South Tom McCall Park was built by the Portland Development Commission and Portland Parks (1999), with accessible beachfront put in place just north of Marquam Bridge. Across Naito Parkway from Waterfront Park is Portland's main business center, with such buildings as the Justice Center, One Main Place, the World Trade Center, and the Mark O. Hatfield Federal Court House, the most expensive public building built in the history of Oregon, opened in 1997.

The Hawthorne's east-end ramps, like those of the Morrison and Burnside, abut Portland's warehouse and produce district. A tangle of railroad tracks interrupt the streets beneath the long approaches to these three bridges. At the bridge's east shore, at river's edge, is Fire Station Seven, the Portland Fire Bureau's Emergency Medical Services office for supplies and administration. This was the home of Portland Fireboat One for more than 40 years, until 1980. A new boat dock opened in 2001 as part of the Vera Katz Eastbank Esplanade. Multnomah County's Bridge Engineering and Maintenance offices, OMSI (and submarine), Willamette River Jet Boats (carrying riders up and down the Willamette since 1997), and the main line of the Union Pacific Railroad are all nearby.

MARQUAM BRIDGE

MARQUAM
river mile 13.5

Opened
4 October 1966 (lower deck)
18 October 1966 (upper deck)

Structure Types
Three-span steel double-deck cantilever truss with suspended section in main span; all spans are Warren trusses. Steel plate girder double-deck approach spans.

Main Span Length
440 feet

Center Height to Water
165 feet (upper deck) 130 feet (lower deck)

Outside Width
57 feet (four lanes southbound; three lanes northbound)

Color
concrete gray

Cost
$14 million

Owner
ODOT

Design Engineers
ODOT

Access
no pedestrians or bicycles

Average Daily Traffic
139,000

Historic American Engineering Record
OR-106

PORTLAND'S FIRST Willamette River freeway bridge, built in the same decade humans first walked on the moon, ushered in the arrival of swift transportation and life in the passing lane. The Marquam, deemed a "transportation corridor," was designed by ODOT for utility rather than beauty. When it opened in 1966 across the Willamette south of downtown, the Marquam closed Oregon's last gap in the Interstate 5 highway from Canada to Mexico. It also completed the first half of the city's inner freeway loop. (The other half, I-405, which crosses the Fremont Bridge two-and-a-half miles to the north, was finished in 1973.)

Among the many who were disenchanted with the appearance of the Marquam and its "spaghetti" ramps were members of the Portland Art Commission. They took their opinion about "the Erector Set bridge" to then Governor Mark O. Hatfield: The Marquam Bridge "is so gross, so lacking in grace, so utterly inconsistent with any concept of esthetics that the Art Commission feels called upon to offer a formal protest."

Others, especially design engineers, did not share that opinion. Before the bridge opened, they noted that it was an example of "simplicity and economy of design," and that it was "unduly criticized for its uncomplicated practicality."

It was built as intended, "to carry the Interstate 5 freeway over the Willamette River in Portland," according to an ODOT fact sheet. Unlike other Portland bridges, the Marquam opened with little public fanfare, the barricades quietly removed. It was completed 28 February 1966; the lower deck opened 4 October, and the upper deck two weeks later. As a result of the public's response to Marquam, the Portland Art Commission would decide the design of Portland's next bridge, Fremont (1973). Aesthetics are not cheap: Fremont Bridge and its approaches cost about six times as much as Marquam's main span.

Packy—the first elephant born at Portland's Washington Park Zoo—turned four in 1966. It was the year President Johnson signed the Freedom of Information Act, *Fahrenheit 451* was a popular film, and the Vietnam War was raging.

Motorists who thought the new bridge wasn't much to look at discovered that it was impressive to look from: the Marquam's sweeping, lofty decks offer an unprecedented

The Marquam Bridge in 1966.

view of west side towers and the river, the Oregon Convention Center and other tall buildings in the Lloyd District, and, in the distance, Mt. Tabor and Mt. Hood. In 1995, construction off Marquam's north side diminished motorists' northwesterly views.

If use is any measure of practicality, almost 140,000 vehicles cross Marquam's decks every day—up from 104,000 vehicles in 1989, when the first edition of this book was published— making it the busiest bridge in Oregon. The number of vehicles using Marquam surpasses the Fremont Bridge, as well as the Interstate, Glenn Jackson, or any other crossing between Oregon and Washington.

Name—The bridge was named for early settler Phillip A. Marquam (1828-1912), an early-day transportation advocate and attorney from Baltimore who settled in Cedar Mill. Before he was elected to the Oregon Legislature in 1882, Marquam was a Multnomah County judge. He built Portland's Marquam Grand Theater, where the Oregon Symphony gave its first concert in 1896. As controversial as the bridge, Marquam was linked with tax fraud in 1907. Earlier, he had lost building and business property in downtown Portland and 80 acres of farm land on Sandy Road through bank foreclosure. Part of his original 298-acre land claim, known as Marquam Hill, is now

The Marquam Bridge as seen from the Willamette Greenway west of OMSI.

140,000 vehicles a day cross the river on Marquam's double decks.

the site of the Oregon Health & Science University and the Veterans Administration Hospital. Marquam is buried in River View Cemetery, Section 15, Lot 253, Grave 2.

Bridge Statistics—Unlike its downstream neighbor, the Hawthorne —with its independent truss spans between piers—the Marquam is a double-deck cantilever truss. All four lanes of the lower deck and three lanes of the upper deck are supported by a main span of 440 feet and two side spans of 301 feet each. The Marquam was the first double-deck vehicle-only bridge built in Oregon. Its construction required 4,000 tons of steel and 9,000 cubic yards of concrete for four piers and two decks. Marquam was the first Portland bridge designed with the help of a computer (approach spans only), and its main span was seismically retrofitted (earthquake proofed) in 1993, with restraining straps installed to tie the approach spans to their piers. The main span was fitted with new, Italian-made bearings, designed to allow the bridge to withstand a moderate earthquake.

Engineers/Builders—The Marquam was designed by ODOT and approved by the Bureau of Public Roads (now the Federal Highway Administration). Contractors were Peter Kiewit Sons' Co. for the concrete piers, and the American Bridge Division of United States Steel Corp., Pittsburgh, for the steel superstructure. The project took five years to complete.

Unusual Note—Glenn L. Jackson, then chairman of the State Highway Commission, responded to the Portland City Council's 1963 inquiry about the absence of pedestrian accommodations on the Marquam. He wrote that in addition to regulations prohibiting foot traffic on all parts of the federal interstate system, "The distance from ground point to ground point [on the bridge] is in excess of one and a quarter miles and it would not be in the public interest nor would it be safe to introduce pedestrian traffic on this structure and the connecting ramps."

Approaches—East end: I-5, I-84, Water Avenue. West end: I-5, 1-405, Macadam Avenue (Highway 43). In 1990, the structure's east and west approach lanes were expanded from three ten-foot, six-inch travel lanes to four 12-foot travel lanes with six-foot shoulders. This widening was made possible by taking the ramps of the unbuilt Mt. Hood Freeway. A new two-lane off-ramp to I-84 and Water Avenue was added at the east side. The changes helped. In the years following the reconstruction, no fatalities were reported on Marquam, with the accident rate dropping to half of what it was before the improvements. On 12 May 2006, a 2001 Ford F-350 pickup headed northbound on Interstate 5 careened up and over a three-foot barrier on the top deck of the Marquam Bridge at mid-span and dove 165 feet into the Willamette River. The body of the driver, 34-year-old Jerry Tupper, was recovered from the Willamette a week later. This was the first reported incident of any vehicle going over the side of the Marquam Bridge in its 40-year history.

The view of Portland is big from the Marquam Bridge.

Neighborhood/Landmarks—Under the east end of the Marquam's main span is the Oregon Museum of Science and Industry and the Willamette Greenway Trail. SamTrak, the open-air excursion train between OMSI and Sellwood, stopped running in 2003. Under the westside approaches is the 409-acre North Macadam District, which includes train tracks used by the Willamette Shore Trolley (WST) to operate between RiverPlace and Lake Oswego. The northern terminus for the WST was moved south to S.W. Bancroft Street (near the Old Spaghetti Factory), so that the Portland Streetcar could be extended. The Portland Streetcar extension from RiverPlace to Gibbs opened for riders in September 2006, to connect with the new Portland Aerial Tram's bottom landing. The streetcar is scheduled to extend to S.W. Lowell Street (one block north of Bancroft) in 2007. WST continues to operate on a seasonal schedule between S.W. Bancroft and Lake Oswego.

West approach ramps of Marquam Bridge as they appear at ground level looking east.

74

ROSS ISLAND BRIDGE

ROSS ISLAND
river mile 14.0

Opened
21 December 1926

Structure Types
Five-span steel cantilever deck truss with arch-shaped main span and no suspended section; side spans are sub-divided Warren trusses. Reinforced concrete girder approach spans.

Main Span Length
535 feet

Center Height to Water
123 feet

Outside Width
52 feet (four traffic lanes, with one 5-foot sidewalk)

Color
"phthalo" blue

Cost
$1.9 million
rehabilitation 2000-2001, $12.5 million

Owner
ODOT; built by Multnomah County

Design Engineer
Gustav Lindenthal, New York

Access
pedestrians, bicycles allowed

Average Daily Traffic
70,000

Historic American Engineering Record
OR-102

The Ross Island was the first "downtown" river bridge in Portland's history to be built without streetcar tracks. It paved the way for Foster Road (diverging from Powell Boulevard at S.E. 50th Avenue) to become a major auto thoroughfare to downtown Portland. By the time the Ross Island was built, progress had come to town. In the nine years between the opening of the Broadway Bridge in 1913 and approval of the 1920s bridges, passenger vehicle registration in Oregon jumped from 13,957 to 123,494. Voters, concerned with the growing number of cars, approved a bridge-building program that has not been duplicated since. The Sellwood opened on 15 December 1925; six months later, a new Burnside opened 28 May 1926; and within seven more months, the Ross Island opened 21 December 1926. Downstream, the Peninsula Bridge Co. was formed in 1924 to promote the St. Johns Bridge, and upstream, the arch span in Oregon City opened 28 December 1922.

The Ross Island Bridge and surrounding neighborhoods in 1928.

Calvin Coolidge was at mid-term of his presidency, and it was the decade of the Nineteenth Amendment—women could vote. Following Charles A. Lindbergh's solo flight to France, as part of his celebratory tour of the United States, he flew the *Spirit of St. Louis* into Portland within a few months of the Ross Island's opening.

Built by Multnomah County but owned and maintained by ODOT since 1976, the Ross Island begins the state's Mount Hood Highway System. U.S. Highway 26 crosses the bridge, and at mid-span Mount Hood is 66 miles east. To the west, U.S. 101 along the Oregon coast intersects with U.S. 26 near Seaside. Pedestrians have always had access to the Ross Island, but in 1958, the sidewalk on the south side of the bridge was removed to widen the bridge for vehicles. The north sidewalk remains.

Name—The Ross Island takes its name from the 304-acre island group located south of the span. The three-island group was named

Oak Islands in 1841, but that name did not prevail. Sherry Ross (1824-67), a pioneer settler from Indiana, filed a land claim in 1850 to farm the largest island, and it soon took his name. Although he was married, Ross was sympathetic to his neighbors in the Oregon wilderness. Portland's population in 1851 numbered 1,927, but only about 20 percent were female. In 1852 Ross wrote to an inquiring relative planning to migrate: "You will do the young men of this country a great favor if you will bring a number of ladys with you." He died at age 42 while visiting California, almost 60 years before the bridge was built.

Upstream from the Ross Island Bridge looking north from the west bank of the Willamette River.

Ross Island's center span trusses cantilever from the river piers to provide maximum height clearance for river traffic.

Erecting Ross Island Bridge trusses on timber falsework, ca. 1926.

Bridge Statistics—The Ross Island is a cantilever deck truss bridge, even though it appears to be an arch. Each end of the bridge is anchored to the shore and the other end—the center—protrudes out from the piers without the need for further support—thus cantilevered. Because it does not have a suspended span connected to the cantilever arms, it is often mistaken as a steel deck arch, similar to Fremont Bridge. In fact, it is a semi-continuous cantilever, like the Queensboro Bridge (a through truss) across the East River in New York, also designed by Gustav Lindenthal. The omission of Ross Island's suspended span saved on materials and allowed for maximum clearance. The 535-foot main span is flanked by four 321-foot steel deck truss spans and 29 concrete approach spans, yielding a total structure length of more than 3,729 feet. As with the Sellwood, Ross Island's trusses (Warren-type with verticals, subdivided panels, and arched lower chords) are below the road deck. In addition to its unique structural design, the balustrade railing contributes to the Ross Island's style. Traffic statistics for the Ross Island, the heaviest traveled of Portland's non-freeway bridges, show the bridge carried nearly 70,000 vehicles a day in 2004. With about 80 percent of Portland's population living on the eastside, vehicles traveling westbound and eastbound number about the same on any given day. In addition, TriMet buses make more than 430 trips across the bridge, carrying 9,000-plus riders.

Ross Island underwent a 19-month $12.5 million rehabilitation that ended in 2001. Prior to the project, the historic concrete railing was not up to standards for crash resistance and portions of the sidewalk were crumbling. The drainage system was permanently clogged, causing storm water to pool on the bridge and

Meeting of Ross Island's cantilever spans, 1926.

run off into the Willamette River. The bridge deck hadn't been paved since 1985 and the surface was showing wear. Failure of the joint seals allowed moisture to seep through, causing rust and ongoing deterioration that undermined the structural integrity of the bridge. Construction crews built a new concrete railing based on the original design, reinforced by two parallel crash-resistant steel tubes running horizontally along the inside of the railing. The bridge deck received a new microsilica concrete overlay. The bridge joints, seals, and bearings were also replaced or repaired, and the bridge drainage system was upgraded to take water off the bridge into environmentally friendly retention/treatment facilities. The bridge lighting has also been updated. ODOT designed the repairs and Mowat Construction was prime contractor.

Engineers/Builders—Gustav Lindenthal designed the Ross Island Bridge (also see Broadway, Burnside, and Sellwood bridges, and glossary). Houghtaling and Dougan Architects, Portland, designed the original bridge railing. Prime contractors were Booth and Pomeroy (main river spans) and Lindstrom & Feigenson (approach structures). Other contractors included Edlefsen-Weygandt, Parker-Schram, and Pacific Bridge. American Bridge Co. fabricated the steel.

Unusual Note—There are six water transport systems across the Willamette River, but the Ross Island is one of only two lower Willamette River bridges (with the Abernethy Bridge) to carry water pipes on its superstructure. The other water pipes are under the river. During the Ross

Ross Island Bridge looking east.

Ironworkers connecting a truss chord on the Ross Island Bridge, ca. 1926. Note precarious footing.

Island's dedication ceremonies, seven-year-old Rosina Corbett broke a bottle of "pure water" against the bridge. Two 24-inch mains, added in 1930, carry millions of gallons of water daily 35 miles from the Bull Run Reservoir to Portland's westside.

Approaches—East end: Powell Boulevard, McLoughlin Boulevard (Highway 99-E). West end: Arthur Street, Barbur Blvd., Naito Parkway.

Neighborhood/Landmarks—Underneath the bridge's west end are tracks for the Portland Streetcar and Zidell Explorations, Inc. (1915), a Portland family-owned business specializing in the manufacture of large, ocean-going barges. Beyond Zidell's yard is the new South Waterfront development, with Oregon Health & Science University's campus and terminus for the OHSU Tram. Here, too, are great blue herons, Portland's official bird. A grouping of more than 60 nests can be seen on Ross Island from the Willamette River Greenway. According to *Wild in the City, A Guide to Portland's Natural Areas*, the herons had nested on Ross Island for more than 20 years until February 2000, when local bald eagles decided to move nearer to the heronry inside the Ross Island lagoon. By March 2000, the herons had moved to the new neighborhood of East Island, just east of Ross Island. They have now moved once again to the downstream tip of Ross Island, although there were a few new nests again on East Island in the spring of 2006. According to Portland Audubon's Mike Houck, they can be easily seen from the bridge itself, but the best view is from the Springwater on the Willamette Trail (on the east side of the Willamette), just upstream from the bridge.

SELLWOOD BRIDGE

SELLWOOD
river mile 16.5

Opened
15 December 1925

Structure Types
Four-span continuous deck truss; all spans are sub-divided Warren trusses. Reinforced concrete approach spans.

Main Span Length
300 feet

Center Height to Water
75 feet

Outside Width
28 feet (two traffic lanes, with one 4-foot northerly sidewalk)

Color
green

Cost
$541,000
approach reconstruction 1980, $950,000

Owner
Multnomah County

Design Engineers
Gustav Lindenthal, New York (truss spans);
Ira G. Hedrick, Portland (approach spans and substructure)

Access
pedestrians, bicycles allowed

Average Daily Traffic
30,500

THE FIRST FIXED-SPAN BRIDGE IN PORTLAND WAS THE SELLWOOD BRIDGE, completed in 1925. It was joined the following year by another fixed-span bridge, the Ross Island. (Both were preceded by the fixed-span Oregon City Bridge in 1922.) Until the 1920s, all of the Portland-proper Willamette River vehicle bridges had one thing in common: they moved, but these newer Willamette River crossings were built high enough so that, according to a newspaper report, "no draw tied up anxious motorists while a chugging tug and mud scow passed up or down stream."

There were no bridges across the Willamette River in Portland when Henry L. Pittock's Sellwood Real Estate Co. filed on 12 July 1882 the plat of what is now the community of Sellwood. It took another 40 years for the namesake bridge to be completed, with its proximity to Eastmoreland and Westmoreland. South Portland residents grumbled for many of those years about the queue

The Spokane Street Ferry shuttled traffic across the river before the bridge.

cross the Willamette River between the Sellwood and the Oregon City Bridge for another 45 years, until the strapping I-205 Abernethy arrived at river mile 25.4 in 1970.

Multnomah County is still the owner of Sellwood Bridge, which has reached the end of its life from both a structural perspective and traffic-carrying capacity. Out of a possible score of 100, Sellwood's sufficiency rating is 2 (bridges rated below 50 are generally recommended for replacement). This is not good, since the Sellwood Bridge is the busiest

Timber falsework used to support truss spans during erection.

for the Spokane Street Ferry. The public boat launch on the Staff Jennings property is the site of what was the ferry's westside ramp. Looking across the river today, one can easily imagine the ferry waiting to take on pedestrians hurrying down the steep grade of Spokane Street. It is ironic that while the Sellwood was an innovative fixed span, it was designed and built too narrow. The Sellwood was inadequate from the day it opened for motorists crossing the bridge westbound to downtown attractions such as McElroy's Ballroom and the Blue Mouse Theater, and eastbound to Oaks Amusement Park or the area sawmills.

A 1925 newspaper story read: "As a pre-Christmas surprise, two oil companies operating in Portland announced last night that the price of gasoline would be raised one cent to 20 cents a gallon." That gasoline was being burned by autos listed in the "want ads" of *The Oregonian*: Hupmobiles, Maxwells, Overlands, Pierce Arrows, Oaklands, Franklins, and Willys-Knights.

Nearly three and a half river miles south, the Southern Pacific Railroad Bridge (bought by Union Pacific Railroad through its acquisition of SPRR in 1996) had been operating 15 years. No other bridge would

Sellwood Bridge dedication plaque.

Sellwood Bridge truss joint and support bearing.

two-lane bridge in Oregon (30,000 vehicles a day crossed the bridge in 2005). Maximum bridge loads were reduced to ten tons in 2004, forcing about 1,400 trucks and buses each day to use an alternate river crossing. The bridge's western approach is settling and sliding, a condition dating to the bridge's earliest days. In an inspection in 2004, performed by Burgess & Niple and evaluated by David Evans & Associates, large cracks were discovered in the concrete approach spans. These were reinforced with steel plates. During an inspection in 2004, additional cracks were discovered at the bridge's east end. Other conditions that contribute to the bridge's low sufficiency are that it is not designed to resist earthquake force, its two traffic lanes are narrow with no center median or shoulders, tight curves at the west end cannot accommodate large vehicles, and the bridge has only one (narrow) sidewalk. Studies by Metro Regional Government estimated the cost in 1998 of replacing the bridge at between $45 million and $60 million for a new two-lane bridge that would accommodate bicyclists and pedestrians. Multnomah County's Capital Improvement Plan calls for replacement of the structure. The County will also explore the feasibility of rehabilitating the existing bridge. Some of the issues being considered include neighborhood livability, coordination with the Southeast Tacoma Street Plan, right-of-way impacts, construction closure (short, long or none?), and how to fund. Especially how to fund: Preliminary cost estimates for the project range from $40 million for rehabilitation to $140 million for replacement. Multnomah County has enough money to begin planning and environmental work on the project in 2006.

The Sellwood Bridge features four-span continuous truss construction.

Name—The bridge was named for the town that was originally settled by South Carolina native Rev. James R. W. Sellwood (1808-94) and was annexed to Portland in 1893. Sellwood had answered the appeal of the bishop of the Episcopal diocese of the new Oregon Territory for "missionaries to work in the frontier field." He is buried in Lone Fir Cemetery, Block 8, Lot 60, Grave 1 North.

Bridge Statistics—The Sellwood Bridge is the only four-span continuous truss highway bridge in Oregon—not unlike a very long log supported by five tall rocks. It may be the only four-span continuous truss in the United States. The bridge is unusual for its asymmetrical vertical curve which gives a neat transition from flat land at its east end to the steeply sloping west end. Sellwood is the first metropolitan span to be built without trolley tracks and the first fixed span. From 1887 until 1925, all major Portland bridges across water moved, including the first and second Morrison, first and second Steel, first and second Madison, Hawthorne, Broadway, three 1908 North Portland railroad bridges, and the Interstate Bridge.

Engineers/Builders—The first proposed design was by the firm Hedrick & Kremers. The final design was by Gustav Lindenthal. Gilpin

Construction of Portland was the contractor, with the steel fabricated by Judson Manufacturing Co. of Emeryville, California.

Unusual Note—Drawings in the Wilson Rare Book Room at the Multnomah County Central Library in Portland show a two-lane Sellwood Bridge designed by engineering consultants Hedrick & Kremers. This Portland duo was fired and replaced by Lindenthal in 1925 during the infamous bridge-kickback scandal that also involved Ross Island and Burnside bridges. Hedrick & Kremers had proposed that Sellwood be constructed using two truss spans from the 1894 Burnside, then being replaced. After his arrival, Lindenthal threw out the recycle scheme, though recycling bridges was common at the time. However, he had to stay within the constraints of budget. It appears the master engineer, who had a wide-ranging design palette, saved money on steel by configuring Sellwood as an all-new four-span continuous truss. The through trusses from the 1894 Burnside Bridge were recycled, both still in use today as bridges in Clackamas County. For more about the Clackamas bridges see *Historic Highway Bridges of Oregon*.

Approaches—East end: Tacoma Street. West end: Macadam Avenue (Highway 43). Sellwood Bridge is considered a "regional" structure

Sellwood Bridge looking west toward the Tualatin Mountains (West Hills).

Steel approach girders recycled from 1894 Burnside Bridge.

because it is used by Clackamas, Washington, and Multnomah County drivers, connecting highways 99E (McLoughlin Boulevard) and 224 (to Clackamas) with Highway 43 (Macadam Avenue).

Neighborhood/Landmarks—Near the bridge's east end is Oaks Amusement Park, built in 1905 by the trolley company serving the area to induce passengers to ride on its cars. The 44-acre park is known for its 96-foot Ferris wheel and skating rink, which has the largest wood skating floor on the West Coast. Also near the east end is the southern perimeter of the Willamette Greenway Trail, Sellwood Riverfront Park, the Oaks Bottom Wildlife Refuge, and the historic Oaks Pioneer Church, dating to 1851.

The 350-acre River View Cemetery, founded in 1882, is located above the bridge's west end. Ellis Lawrence, who founded the University of Oregon's School of Architecture in 1914, designed the caretaker's residence. The caretaker's building is now used by the cemetery staff.

THE SELLWOOD BRIDGE POEM

Is it my fault
that I am not able
to stand perfectly straight
and be perfectly stable?
I didn't design me
I had no say
I would be different
if I had my way!
I'd be like the Morrison
if I could be changed
instead of myself
who feels so deranged.
I would have lights
that make the night glow.
They would make neat designs
and put up a show.
People would watch me
all through the night
as I put up my patterns
they make quite a sight.
So please do not mock me
and make me feel shame.
It isn't my fault
it's the makers to blame.

Nathan Baptiste

Mike McCarroll's sixth grade class
Uplands Elementary, Lake Oswego, Oregon
1995

ABERNETHY BRIDGE

ABERNETHY
river mile 25.4

Opened
3 May 1970

Structure Types
Steel box girders and steel plate girders

Main Span Length
430 feet

Center Height to Water
85 feet

Outside Width
100 feet (six 12-foot traffic lanes)

Color
green

Cost
$15.9 million
seismic retrofit 2001-2002, $7 million

Owner
ODOT

Design Engineers
Moffatt, Nichol & Bonney, Portland

Access
no pedestrians or bicycles

Average Daily Traffic
102,400

Historic American Engineering Record
none

THE ABERNETHY, at river mile 25.4, is only a half-mile north (downstream) of the Oregon City Bridge, but it is light years away in appearance and purpose. In 2004, more than 102,000 vehicles funneled across its six 12-foot lanes at interstate speeds. Its freeway design, steep ascension, and side barriers keep motorists ignorant: the bridge blends in so well with the approaches and the adjoining freeway that travelers, who cross it in less than a minute, may not know they are on a bridge. While it is called the Abernethy by some ODOT engineers, schematic drawings designate it the "Willamette River West Linn Bridge." Others refer to it as the "I-205 Bridge," or the "Oregon City Freeway Bridge." On traffic count records, it is referred to as the East Portland Freeway at milepost 9.12. Considering that its main span is about the same length as the Marquam and that it is nearly 20 feet wider than Fremont, by any name this bridge is an imposing landmark.

Historic view of the Abernethy Bridge featuring an inset of Tom Edwards, Oregon State Highway Engineer in 1972. The Oregon City Bridge is in the foreground.

90

Side view of the Abernethy Bridge.

When it opened 30 May 1970, "awareness" was the byword of the day—that year cigarette ads were banned from television and radio. The right to vote was granted to 18-year-olds, and for the first time, women could be appointed the rank of general in the U.S. military. In New York City, *Hello Dolly* was in rehearsal for its opening on Broadway, and the first tenants were occupying the lower floors of the World Trade Center's North Tower. In Portland, Johns Landing was developing along Macadam Avenue.

Name—Born in New York City, George Abernethy (1807-77) came to the Northwest with a missionary party. He was elected the provisional governor of the Oregon Territory in 1845. After his official duties ended, he went into the dry goods business in Oregon City, where he prospered and associated with the powerful of the day, including, some say, the less than honorable. Abernethy reportedly was involved in the land deal that defrauded the former Hudson's Bay Company chief factor John McLoughlin of his rightful claim to sawmills and gristmills (known as the Island Mills) on the Willamette River, near Oregon City. Abernethy eventually lost most of his fortune and moved to Portland in 1871. He died six years later, and is buried in River View Cemetery, Section 15, Lot 253, Grave 2.

Bridge Statistics—Plate girder simple spans, plate girder continuous spans, and steel box girder continuous spans combine to support the deck of this 2,727-foot-long bridge. Three continuous steel box girder spans of 300, 430, and 300 feet cross the main channel of the river. These girders are, according to the plans, "parabolically haunched" at the piers, varying in depth from 15 feet to 21 feet. The parabolic or "curved" design gives extra depth at the piers, increasing support and adding strength, thus allowing longer beams to be used in the structure. Four of these box girders are supported on slender twin-shaft concrete piers, each pair of girders supporting three lanes of the roadway. Overall, there are 15 spans and

60 girders. What is not obvious is that the superstructure (main span) was designed to be two separate bridges with a median barrier running the length of the center span. In addition, a water pipe runs between the northbound and southbound structures across the river, making this the second aqueduct bridge (with Ross Island) on the lower Willamette.

The Abernethy required 23 million pounds of structural steel, 6.5 million pounds of reinforcing steel, and more than 30,000 cubic yards of concrete. Each of the sculptured concrete piers is dimensionally different; forms for each had to be fabricated separately.

There are hundreds of seismic retrofits needed in the metropolitan area and around Oregon. With its limited funds (and no budget for fully earthquake-proofing any of Oregon's bridges), ODOT selected the Abernethy, Marquam, and St. Johns bridges to be retrofitted because they are major bridges over major water crossings. In addition, Abernethy is a designated Regional Emergency Transportation Route. It was seismically retrofitted in a two-year upgrade that ended in 2002, giving it protection for a moderate earthquake in the Portland area. Fixes on the main river and approach spans include cable ties, replacement of some of the bridge's bearings, and restraints added to some of the bearings. Cost for

Elevation view of the Abernethy Bridge.

The Abernethy Bridge is two separate bridges with a median barrier running the length of the center span.

the retrofit was approximately $7 million and included a companion contract for installing an access walkway and water pipe between the bridge's northbound and southbound halves.

Engineers/Builders—Moffatt, Nichol & Bonney of Portland designed the Abernethy for ODOT (see Morrison Bridge). The contractor was Willamette River Constructors, a joint venture between Willamette-Western Corp., a division of Riedel International, and Donald M. Drake Co. of Portland. The construction of the Abernethy Bridge began in 1968. While foundation and pier work were in progress, structural steel members for the superstructure were fabricated in Seattle and Vancouver, Washington. The completed welded steel sections were shipped to the bridge site by barge, railroad, and truck.

Unusual Note—In 1974 the Optimist Club of Oregon City erected a railing around an elm tree that had been planted in 1850 near the end of the Oregon Trail by the wife of Governor George Abernethy. The Abernethy Bridge was originally sited to pass through the tree, but ODOT, realizing the tree's significance, moved the bridge slightly to the south to allow it to survive. The huge elm was cut down in June 2001, after it split from its own weight and became a safety hazard.

Approaches—East end: I-205, McLoughlin Boulevard (Highway 99-E). West end: I-205, Willamette Drive (Highway 43).

The bridge is part of the I-205 bypass route built to siphon traffic from the I-5 corridor as it passes through Portland. Turning off I-5 south of Portland, the East Portland Freeway (I-205) swings eastward, passes through the communities of West Linn and Oregon City (connected by the Abernethy Bridge), turns northerly through the eastside of Portland, and finally crosses the Columbia River (over the Glenn Jackson Bridge) to rejoin I-5 north of Vancouver, Washington.

On the west end of the bridge there are on- and off-ramps to Willamette Drive (Highway 43), which passes underneath; the Pacific Highway (99-E) connects on the east side.

Neighborhood/Landmark—On a spring day, there may be as many as a hundred fishing boats on the river beneath the Abernethy Bridge. Downstream is Clackamette Park, the last put-in option for boaters before reaching Willamette Falls. Situated at the confluence of the Willamette and Clackamas rivers, the 22-acre park often floods.

OREGON CITY BRIDGE

OREGON CITY
river mile 25.9

Opened
28 December 1922

Precursor
1888 pedestrian bridge

Structure Types:
Steel half-through arch. Reinforced concrete girder and steel plate girder approach spans.

Main Span Length
360 feet

Center Height to Water
49 feet

Outside Width
28 feet (two traffic lanes, with two 4½-foot sidewalks)

Color
concrete gray

Cost
$300,000

Owner
ODOT

Design Engineer
Conde B. McCullough (ODOT)

Access
pedestrians, bicycles allowed

Average Daily Traffic
14,000

Historic American Engineering Record
OR-31

THE DETAILING on the Oregon City Bridge—pylons, ornate bridge railings, arched fascia curtain walls, fluted Art Deco main piers, and the use of bush-hammered inset panels—are the special touches of Oregon's famous bridge design engineer, Conde B. McCullough. Though several of the lower Willamette River bridges are eligible for the National Register of Historic Places, the Oregon City Bridge is the only one actually listed in the Register—added in 2005. It is also the only lower Willamette River bridge designed by McCullough, best known for his magnificent Oregon Coast Highway bridges. The Oregon City structure, southernmost of the Portland-area river spans, gracefully arches across the wash of Willamette Falls at river mile 25.9. Before Portland's three 1920s bridges were built, Clackamas County voters approved the replacement of the 1888 pedestrian suspension bridge at their falls. The extant bridge opened in 1922 and was the last link in the Pacific Highway stretching from Canada to Mexico. It is the last span across the Willamette River until the I-5 bridge at Wilsonville, 15 miles upstream, yet in 2004 it carried fewer than 14,000 vehicles a day.

Looking west on the deck of the Oregon City Bridge.

The Oregon City Bridge replaced this pedestrian suspension bridge featuring wooden support towers.

The Oregon City Bridge in the old days, before retaining walls.

Name—Oregon City was laid out and named in 1842 by Dr. John McLoughlin of Hudson's Bay Company fame. The initial name of the locality was Willamette or Willamette Falls.

Bridge Statistics—This 745-foot-long, 28-foot-wide steel half-through arch bridge has a main span of 360 feet. It is encased in sprayed-on concrete (shotcrete) to protect it from corrosive fumes discharged by nearby paper mills. The gray shotcrete makes it look like a concrete arch, one of its designer's favorite forms. It is one of four half-through arch designs in the state. The first bridge to span this section of the Willamette River was a suspension bridge, with wooden support towers for the cables. It opened in 1888, and replaced an expensive toll ferry. According to one study, this was the first true suspension bridge west of the Rocky Mountains. The suspension cables of the old bridge supported the arch ribs on the new bridge until all segments were erected and self-supporting.

Engineers/Builders—In addition to his work on the Oregon City Bridge, Conde B. McCullough (1887-1946) designed the Yaquina Bay and Alsea Bay bridges, the steel cantilever bridge over Coos Bay, and other major and minor spans along the Oregon Coast Highway. As an Oregon State Bridge Engineer, McCullough was responsible for more than 500 Oregon bridges and is best known for his work with reinforced concrete bridges. McCullough's John McLoughlin (arch) Bridge, opened in 1933 across the mouth of the Clackamas River, was rated as the most beautiful steel bridge in its class by the American Institute of Steel Construction. McCullough also worked on the design and construction of bridges in

The Oregon City Bridge gracefully arches across the wash of Willamette Falls.

Panama, Guatemala, El Salvador, Honduras, and Costa Rica.

The identifying plate on the Oregon City structure's west end reads: "A.B. Guthrie & Co., Inc. Contractors—Willamette River Bridge, built by Oregon City, West Linn, Clackamas County, State of Oregon." It's now owned and maintained by ODOT.

Unusual Note—Both piers were designed with elaborate public restroom facilities. The deck widens at the piers to make room for the stairways that descend to the restrooms. Unfortunately, due to vandalism, the restrooms have been closed to the public since 1937.

Approaches—East end: Seventh Street, Main Avenue (McLoughlin Boulevard runs north-south beneath the bridge). West end: Willamette Falls Drive (Highway 43).

Neighborhood/Landmarks—The east end of the bridge reaches into the heart of Oregon City, population about 30,000 in 2003. Motorists crossing the bridge from west to east have a nearly perfect view of the Oregon City municipal elevator, which carries passengers 130 feet up

The Oregon City Bridge looking east toward Oregon City.

the bluff located at the end of Seventh Street. (The original elevator, built in 1912, was water-powered. The present structure was dedicated in 1955.)

On the west end of the bridge is West Linn, population 25,000, and the Willamette Falls Locks (1873), now the oldest operating navigational locks in the U.S. The footbridge across the locks is a small single-leaf bascule, opened in 1925. Few users, mostly paper mill workers, realize that the footbridge is a second Portland-area Joseph Strauss-designed bascule bridge (see Burnside Bridge and glossary for more about Strauss, responsible for San Francisco's Golden Gate Bridge). For a closer look at how river traffic is transported around this major falls, follow the sign on the west end of the footbridge that reads, "The painted footsteps lead to the locks." A 40-foot drop, Willamette Falls, described as "small Niagara," is affected by the Pacific Ocean tides. The falls are lighted, so the action can be viewed at night. The towering stacks of the Oregon City and West Linn pulp and paper mills are nearby. Also constant are the boats and poles of anglers casting for sturgeon and Chinook salmon between the Oregon City and Abernethy bridges.

SAUVIE ISLAND – Existing Bridge

SAUVIE ISLAND
On the Multnomah Channel where the Willamette River splits at river mile 3

Opened
30 December 1950

Structure Types
Three steel truss spans with Parker through truss main span and two Warren deck truss side spans. Reinforced concrete girder approach spans.

Main Span Length
200 feet

Center Height to Water
80 feet

Outside Width
41 feet (two traffic lanes, with a four-foot sidewalk on each side)

Color
ODOT green

Cost
$900,000

Owner
Multnomah County

Design Engineers
Oregon State Highway Department

Contractor
Gilpin Construction

Access
pedestrians, bicycles allowed

Average Daily Traffic
3,800

SAUVIE ISLAND BRIDGE WAS THE FIRST MAJOR RIVER BRIDGE built in Portland after World War II. Located across the Multnomah Channel (also called the Willamette Slough) of the Willamette River, this two-lane truss was built to replace the Sauvie Island Ferry. It was designed by the Oregon State Highway Department. Multnomah County assumed ownership and maintenance of the bridge in 1951, after the last detail of the bridge's completion. As this edition is written, a second Sauvie island Bridge is being built by the County to replace the 1950 bridge. The new bridge is scheduled to open in 2008. About ten miles northwest of downtown Portland, the Sauvie Island Bridge connects U.S. Highway 30 to Sauvie Island. Sixteen miles long and about four miles wide, the 24,000-acre island is located in Columbia and Multnomah counties and is the largest island on the Columbia River.

SAUVIE ISLAND
New Bridge

SAUVIE ISLAND
On the Multnomah Channel where the Willamette River splits at river mile 3 (upriver from the 1950 bridge)

Opening Date
2008

Structure Types
Steel tied arch main span. Prestressed concrete box girder approach spans.

Main Span Length
360 feet

Center Height to Water
80 feet

Outside Width
66 feet, with two 12-foot travel lanes, two six-foot shoulders, two six-foot sidewalks

Color
weathering steel

Cost
$38 million (projected)

Owner
Multnomah County

Design Engineers
David Evans & Associates, Portland and Salem, Oregon

Architect
H2L2 Architecture, New York

Contractor
Max J. Kuney Co.

Access
pedestrians, bicycles allowed

Average Daily Traffic
To be determined

Photo-simulation of the new Sauvie Island Bridge, slated for completion in 2008.

Sauvie Island, with its own rivers, sloughs, lakes, and islands, combines agriculture, industry, and homes, as well as significant natural and recreational resources in a rural landscape. The Sauvie Island Bridge is critical to the island community because it provides the only vehicular access to the mainland. About 1,300 people now live here. It was first inhabited by Native American Chinookan people and its history includes explorations by the British, a visit by Lewis and Clark in November 1806, a fort and trading post, a dairy farm established by the Hudson's Bay Company in 1836, and flood control dikes and levees built 1938-1941 by the US Army Corps of Engineers. The oldest human-made structure is the 1858 Bybee-Howell House, listed in the National Register of Historic Places in 1974 but no longer open to the public. Part of Metro's 93-acre Howell Territorial Park, this pioneer homestead features a farm museum, orchard, and picnic area. Farming has continued to be the island's main activity, but industry on the island's southern tip includes the Alder Creek Lumber Co. mill. Almost half of the island (entire northern portion) is owned by the Oregon Department of Fish and Wildlife, which manages a habitat for hundreds of species of birds and maintains a wildlife area. Sauvie Island is also a popular bicycling destination, with several sandy beaches for day camping, swimming, fishing, kayaking, and boating. Attractions also include Wapato State Park, the Pumpkin Patch, and other seasonal farm businesses and produce stands. The number of visitors has doubled in the past ten years, from 750,000 to 1.5 million. Competition between motor vehicles and bicycles for space on island roads is common. At times, long traffic lines back up to cross the narrow Sauvie Island Bridge. When the bridge opened in 1950, the first modern credit cards and *Peanuts* and *Dennis the Menace* cartoon strips were being introduced. This was the year the Korean War began, CBS broadcast in color to 25 television sets, and the first Xerox photocopiers rolled off the assembly line.

During an inspection in December 2001, the County found large cracks in the bridge's concrete approach spans. As a result, restrictions were placed on the weight and speed of vehicles using the bridge. After a second inspection by David Evans & Associates, emergency repairs were made in early 2002. By current federal and state standards, the bridge's sufficiency rating is 6 out of a possible rating of 100, and it has been classified as functionally obsolete and structurally deficient. With the temporary repairs, it can carry loads of no more than 40 tons. However, even with the temporary repairs, the 1950 bridge is inadequate to meet the needs of the island's farmers and industrial businesses, is substandard for bicyclists and pedestrians, and is at the end of its service life at this location.

Preliminary design for the new bridge was presented in July 2004, after a year of meetings between Multnomah County, Sauvie Island residents and business owners, and a citizens advisory committee, which helped develop the bridge's aesthetic details. Included in this process were the recommendations of H2L2, an architectural firm based in New York City. County Commissioner Maria Rojo de Steffey and others worked to find

funding for the new bridge, projected to cost $38 million. Money is coming from Multnomah County, Fiscal Year 2002/2003 Federal Transportation Appropriation funds, Oregon Transportation Investment Act, and the Highway Bridge Repair and Replacement program. Ground-breaking for the new bridge, built on a new alignment located directly upstream (south) of the old bridge, took place 4 January 2006.

Name—Sauvie Island was named for Laurent Sauvé, who managed a dairy

established by the Hudson Bay Co. in 1836. According to Catholic Church Records of the Pacific Northwest (*St. Paul* Volume), Laurent Sauvé spent ten years at the dairy before retiring to French Prairie in 1844. His burial site is unknown. When Lewis and Clark visited the island in 1806, they named it Wapato Island. A major Native American residential site, Sauvie Island was a source of the wapato plant (*Sagittaria latifolia*). This wild potato was a diet mainstay. The island has also been called Multnomah Island and Wyeth Island.

New bridge column construction and inspection of 1950 bridge.

Preservationists propose to reuse the Sauvie Island Bridge as a bicycle- and pedestrian-only bridge in another location.

Bridge Statistics—The 1950 bridge, of riveted construction, consists of a 200-foot steel Parker through truss main span, with 200-foot steel Warren deck truss flanking spans and 598 feet of reinforced concrete deck girder spans. The total length is 1,198 feet, placing the Sauvie Island Bridge as the longest post-war (ca. 1945-1955) bridge built in Oregon

with steel truss components as part of its full configuration. According to its National Register of Historic Places nomination data, the Sauvie Island Bridge was the last post-war Parker through truss built in Multnomah County. The main span provides a vertical clearance of about 80 feet above low water and has two 11-foot travel lanes, two-foot

shoulders, and a four-foot sidewalk on each side. The bridge approach from the island includes grades up to seven percent.

The new bridge is a tied arch, similar to the Fremont Bridge and the Union Station Pedestrian Bridge. Main span length is 360 feet, almost twice as long as the old bridge.

1950 Sauvie Island Bridge looking north.

Overall width of the new bridge is 66 feet, compared to the old bridge's width of 41 feet. The extra 25 feet allows for two 12-foot travel lanes, two six-foot shoulders, and two six-foot sidewalks, as opposed to two four-foot sidewalks on the 1950 bridge. The arch portion of the new bridge is constructed of weathering steel—like the lift span and towers of BNSF Railway Bridge 5.1, around the corner. Weathering steel is made with additives that produce a permanent coat of rust. The tight rust coat does not flake off, protecting the underlying steel from air and water, known as oxidation (see glossary).

Engineers/Builders—The 1950 Sauvie Island Bridge was designed under State Bridge Engineer G.S. Paxson. The most pressing design issue was to satisfy the US Army Corps of Engineers that the Willamette Slough (now Multnomah Channel) would remain open to navigation. The bridge construction contract was awarded to the Gilpin Construction Co. of Portland in February 1949 and was completed in April 1951. The 2008 Sauvie Island Bridge was designed for Multnomah County by David Evans & Associates and constructed by Max J. Kuney Co.

Unusual Note—The 1950 bridge is eligible for listing in the National Register of Historic Places, and since there are only about 150 steel truss highway bridges remaining in Oregon, and the main span is a rare Parker truss, preservationists are hoping it can be reused as a bicycle- and pedestrian-only bridge in another location. The 2008 bridge is the first river bridge in the Portland area constructed with drilled shaft foundations. These shafts range up to ten feet in diameter, and reach into the ground by as much as 160 feet. (For more about drilled shafts, see How and Why Bridges Are Built and the glossary.)

Approaches—At its west end, the Sauvie Island Bridge connects with US Highway 30, and at its east end with NW Sauvie Island Road.

Neighborhood/Landmarks—The Sauvie Island Bridge is located ten miles northwest of downtown Portland, on Highway 30. The bridge is four miles northwest of the St. Johns Bridge, located across the Willamette River proper. Views from the bridge include the West Hills (Tualatin Mountains) and the Morse Brothers rock quarry, as well as Mount St. Helens, Mount Hood, Larson's Moorage, Channel Island Marina, floating homes, and pleasure boats, and occasionally the steamer *Portland*.

INTERSTATE BRIDGE

INTERSTATE
river mile 106.5

Opened
14 February 1917 (northbound)
1 July 1958 (southbound)

Structure Types
Each bridge has 11 steel through truss spans with one vertical lift movable main span and ten fixed spans; all spans are Pennsylvania-Petit trusses.

Lift Span Length
279 feet

Height to Water
72 feet at fixed "humpback" spans

Outside Width
38 feet (northbound), 39 feet (southbound)

Color
green

Cost
$1.75 million (1917 span)
$14.5 million (1958 span, and alterations to 1917 bridge)

Owners
States of Oregon and Washington, jointly

Design Engineers
Waddell & Harrington, Kansas City, Missouri (N/B); ODOT (S/B)

Access
pedestrians, bicycles allowed

Bridge Opening Signals
audible: two long, one short
radio call sign: (channel 13) KBM

Average Daily Traffic
130,000 both bridges

RESIDENTS OF VANCOUVER, Washington watched as ten vehicle bridges were built and rebuilt across the Willamette between 1887 and 1913 and longed for their own bridge across the Columbia. *The Oregonian* reported that on 30 June 1905, 2,000 people lined up to cross on the Interstate Ferry to attend Clark County Day at the Lewis and Clark Centennial Exposition and Oriental Fair at Portland's Guilds Lake. Little did they know two bridges loomed in their city's near future.

The first Interstate Bridge opened on Valentine's Day 1917, a joint project between Clark County in Washington and Multnomah County in Oregon financed by bonds. Ten thousand people lived in Vancouver, and Washington had a population of about a million. The census for the entire state of Oregon stood at 600,000 that same year. It did not seem necessary to build anything larger than a four-lane bridge.

During its first year of operation, the speed limit was 15 miles per hour and the bridge opened 1,000 times for water travel. By 1948 openings had doubled, and proposals were being discussed

The Interstate Bridge and the Portland-Vancouver Ferry, ca. 1920.

"Humpback" shape given to the new southbound bridge and the original northbound bridge to accommodate river traffic.

to increase vertical clearance and to construct a second (southbound) span. In 1958, the *Vancouver Columbian* reported the bridge opened a total of 4,225 times—710 of them during rush hours, delaying traffic for a total of 400 hours. Records show that daily highway traffic volume increased from 13,000 in 1936, to 30,000 by 1950.

In 1958, the twin southbound bridge opened (a joint project of Oregon and Washington state highway departments), and the original, now northbound, span was closed for two years of reconstruction. The old span was given a "humpback" to match the new span—a shape that allows most Columbia River traffic to pass under the fixed-span trusses. Interstate is

regularly refurbished and maintained by ODOT, with costs shared 50-50 with Washington DOT. ODOT is also responsible for bridge operations, with Interstate's bridge operators under the supervision of Region One headquarters in Northwest Portland. There are four full-time operators and six more on-call. Interstate Bridge operators perform maintenance as well.

Both the 1917 and 1958 bridges were financed by the coins of commuters at tollbooths. For the first bridge, toll ticket sellers (wearing uniforms they bought) collected five cents for "each person riding on an animal" and the same for those riding in a vehicle. The 1917 bridge was taken over by the Oregon and Washington highways departments in 1928, with tolls removed the following year. For the second bridge, drivers pitched into metal cages 20 cents for cars, 40 cents for light trucks, and 60 cents for heavy trucks and buses. In 1966, when the 1958 bridge was paid off, the last tollbooth closed.

The 1917 bridge was originally part of old Highway 99, running north/south through Oregon and Washington. In 1957, the bridge was officially designated as part of the new Interstate 5 highway system. When the 1958 bridge was finished, it also became part of I-5.

Steps are being taken to improve transportation between Oregon and Washington along the I-5 corridor. Oregon and Washington DOTs are jointly sponsoring the Columbia River Crossing project with the objective of improving mobility, reliability, and accessibility for all types of traffic moving between Portland and Vancouver. Other project participants include the federal government, local governments, and public transit agencies. The study area, five miles of I-5 between SR 500 in Vancouver and Columbia Boulevard in Portland, suffers between four and six hours of congestion a day. Existing transit service is buses, which also get stuck. One question is how to enhance or replace the current twin bridges to meet demands. Possible changes could include modifications to the existing bridges, a new arterial bridge alongside them, or an entirely new I-5 bridge (all with or without light rail or another form of high capacity transit). The final Environmental Impact Statement and Federal Record of Decision are due in 2008.

Interstate remained the sole Portland-area Columbia River vehicle bridge for 65 years, until Glenn Jackson opened upriver (east). In 2006, the twin Interstate carried about 130,000 vehicles a day between Oregon and Washington.

Name—Interstate Bridge, carrying Interstate 5 across the Columbia River between Oregon and Washington, is named for its location.

110

Twin Interstate bridges were built 41 years apart.

Bridge Statistics—In response to two long blasts and one short blast from the horns of river vessels, or to marine radio requests, the bridge operator raises the lift spans on both bridges to allow a 176-foot vertical and a 270-foot horizontal clearance. Vessels with less height can pass beneath the stationary "humpbacks" that provide a 72-foot maximum vertical and 531-foot horizontal clearance. South of mid-channel, smaller traffic can pass under spans that are 58 feet high and 265 feet wide.

During September 1997, the northbound (east) bridge was closed for replacement of counterweight sheaves and steel ropes at the north tower. The $3 million project also mended a cracked axle-like steel trunnion. Between 1999-2001, the northbound bridge was painted, with sub-decking and steel rehabilitated for $17 million. The most recent construction finished in January 2006, with an $11 million electrical upgrade.

Engineers/Builders—Waddell & Harrington, consulting engineers, Kansas City, Missouri (see Hawthorne and Steel bridges) designed the 1917 (northbound) Interstate. When Waddell and Harrington dissolved their partnership in the summer of 1915, Harrington carried

Interstate Bridge looking south from Vancouver toward Portland, with 1917 bridge on near side.

on, joining the firm of Howard & Ash, renamed Harrington, Howard, & Ash. Engineering drawings for the 1917 span, dated 14 December 1914, are stamped "Waddell & Harrington, E.E. Howard and L.R. Ash Associate Engineers, Kansas City, Missouri." Pacific Bridge, of Portland, built the substructure. Porter Brothers, of Portland, erected the spans, with the steel fabricated and furnished by American Bridge (United States Steel Co.). The 1958 (southbound) Interstate Bridge was designed by the Oregon State Highway Department, with construction also managed by OSHD. Washington Highway Department managed the 1958 bridge's mechanical and electrical design and construction. The second bridge generally duplicated plans for the earlier bridge, with some modifications. Ben C. Gerwick, Inc. developed new pier details for the new bridge and modification of the old bridge. Guy F. Atkinson Co. of San Francisco was the general contractor for the 1958 bridge, with Judson Pacific-Murphy of Emeryville, California as the subcontractor for steel fabrication and erection.

Unusual Note—At one time, Interstate Bridge operators, aided by computers, monitored wind velocity and ice build-up on not only the decks of the Interstate Bridge, but also on Glenn Jackson Bridge, Fremont Bridge, and Halsey Street overpass 24 hours a day, summoning sanding trucks and ordering bridge closures. Since 1 January 1996, keeping traffic moving has been the responsibility of ODOT's Traffic Management Operations Center (TMOC—see glossary)

Approaches—North end (Vancouver and Washington state): I-5, State Route 14. South end (North Portland and Oregon state): I-5. I-5 is a 1,400-mile freeway through California, Oregon, and Washington (connecting Mexico and Canada). Integral to that route, three-quarter-mile-long Interstate crosses the Columbia at river mile 106.5 to link Washington and Oregon. Interstate's lift span openings produce the only traffic stops on I-5 from Mexico to Canada. On the south end of Interstate Bridge, just east of the northbound lanes, is a marker with an inscription by Thomas Babington Macauley, an English writer and statesman of the 1800s. It reads: "Of all inventions, the alphabet and the printing press alone excepted, those inventions which abridge distance have done most for the civilization of our species. Every improvement of the means of locomotion benefits mankind morally and intellectually as well as materially, and not only facilitates the interchange of the various productions of nature and art, but tends to move national and provincial antipathies, and to bind together all the branches of the great human

family." The marker, sponsored by the Daughters of the American Revolution, was put there specifically for this bridge, but as the *Columbian* noted in a January 2000 article, "It could be appropriate for all the bridges of greater Portland and for both interstate highway bridges that connect Vancouver with Portland and Washington with Oregon.

BOB SALLINGER AND OTHER STAFF MEMBERS at Portland Audubon work tirelessly to protect peregrines nesting on Portland-area bridges. Efforts include monitoring the falcons, banding nestling falcons, and rescuing young falcons from life threatening crashes into the Willamette or getting hit by cars as they learn to fly. Peregrines began scouting out the Fremont Bridge in 1993 as a place to live. Since that time, Fremont Bridge has become the most productive nest site in the state and peregrines have also established eyries on five other Portland area bridges. Clocked at 200 miles an hour, peregrines are the fastest animals on earth. They were listed under the federal Endangered Species Act as an endangered species from 1973 through 1999. They remain listed as endangered under the State of Oregon Endangered Species Act. This photo was taken on the Interstate Bridge during 2006 peregrine monitoring activities.

GLENN L. JACKSON MEMORIAL BRIDGE

GLENN L. JACKSON
river mile 112.4

Opened
15 December 1982

Structure Type
Segmental prestressed concrete box girder

Main Span Length
600 feet

Center Height to Water
144 feet

Outside Width
150 feet (four 12-foot traffic lanes, each direction; plus 12-foot median containing a 9-foot pedestrian/bicycle walkway)

Color
concrete gray

Cost
$175 million

Owners
States of Oregon and Washington, jointly

Design Engineers
Sverdrup & Parcel, St. Louis (North Channel Bridge);
ODOT (South Channel Bridge)

Access
pedestrians, bicycles allowed

Average Daily Traffic
137,000

ALMOST IMMEDIATELY after the first automobile arrived in the Northwest in 1908, traffic congestion became a problem both in downtown Portland and in Vancouver, Washington. In response to rapidly growing pressure from motorists, the Interstate Bridge was built across the Columbia in 1917 and was doubled in capacity in 1958. Still, commuters between the two cities grumbled louder and louder as they sat in longer and longer lines. By December 1981, approximately 110,000 cars a day were negotiating the twin-span Interstate. The need for an eastside bypass of both cities had been recognized much earlier, and planning for such a crossing had begun in 1950. Finally, it was designated as part of the I-205 (East Portland Freeway) in 1964, and an agreement covering design and construction of the I-205 Bridge was reached by Oregon and Washington in 1969. The actual bridge did not open, however, until 15 December 1982.

The Glenn L. Jackson Memorial Bridge crosses the Columbia River at river mile 112.4. *Engineering News-Record*, which featured the bridge in a cover story, called it "the first of a new generation of large-scale bridges in the United States." The original design of the bridge introduced to American builders a new construction method for concrete bridges called free-cantilever or "balanced" erection. At that time there were no modern concrete segmental bridges in the United States and nothing in the world to rival the Jackson in size, with its deck of more than a million square feet. (Before the Jackson opened, a segmental bridge erected by cantilever, the JFK Causeway, opened in Corpus Christi, Texas, in 1973.)

The largest bridge in the Portland area in overall length, this structure is actually two separate spans, joined down the middle by a nine-foot bike path and walkway.

Construction of north channel piers in the Columbia River.

Unusual construction methods allowed unimpeded river navigation during construction. The north channel crossing was built segment by segment, at the time the largest concrete segments ever cast. The 600-foot main span, 32 feet deep at the piers and 17 feet deep at mid-span, was of cast-in-place segmental construction, post-tensioned, as were the two adjacent spans. Four form travelers were used to cantilever in both directions from two piers simultaneously. The cast-in-place segments are from 12 to 16 feet long. Segments for the remaining 13 north channel spans were precast and individually lifted into place. The segments, some weighing as much as 190 tons, were cast four miles downstream and barged to the site. The south channel crossing spans and the Washington approach spans were cast-in-place on falsework.

Just as impressive as the engineering advances of the Jackson are the population changes that required its construction. From the time the Interstate Bridge opened in 1917 until the Glenn Jackson opened in 1982, Vancouver's population grew from 12,000 to 43,000. In 2006, Vancouver's population is 155,000. Washington state's population grew from one million to five million, and Oregon's population, 600,000 when the Interstate opened, now exceeds 3.6 million.

In 1982, the year the Jackson opened, artificial heart transplants began. Personal computers for the home became a reality. Locally, Bud Clark was still running a neighborhood pub and would not be mayor of Portland for another four years. The Portland Building and Pioneer

Beginning of segmental box girder construction on the Washington side.

The south channel crossing spans were cast-in-place on falsework. Falsework sections were floated into place on barges, then supported on steel piles.

Courthouse Square were under construction, and Pacific Northwest Bell Telephone Co. began transmitting digital information through fiber optic lines.

Name—At ground-breaking ceremonies, held on 23 August 1977, Oregon Governor Bob Straub declared: "Henceforth, the I-205 Bridge over the Columbia River shall be known as the Glenn L. Jackson Bridge." This was in honor of Glenn Jackson (1912-1980), appointed chairman of the Oregon State Highway Commission in 1962. Later, Jackson ended his highly influential career as chairman of Oregon's Economic Development Commission. He was considered one of the most powerful influences on regional development and had a reputation as a man accustomed to getting his way. He is buried in the Jackson family plot, D Lot 33, Block 2, in Willamette Memorial Park Cemetery, located in Millersburg (Albany), Oregon.

Bridge Statistics—To provide separate highways for north- and southbound traffic, twin structures, each 7,460 feet long, stretch between the Washington shore and Oregon's Government Island. Additionally, two structures, each 3,120 feet long, cross the south channel between Government Island and the Oregon mainland. The two pairs of structures are separated by 1,170 feet of fill across the island. The overall bridge length is 11,750 feet.

Engineers/Builders—Sverdrup & Parcel of St. Louis, now Jacobs-Sverdrup (see Morrison Bridge), designed the north channel structure, including the Washington approach. Sverdrup & Parcel's design for the Glenn Jackson won the "Grand Conceptor" award for 1983, the top award presented annually

Aerial shot of entire Glenn Jackson Bridge from the Washington side.

The north channel crossing spans were built segment by segment, at the time the largest concrete segments ever cast.

by the American Consulting Engineers Council, Washington, D.C., for the nation's most innovative engineering structure. The south channel crossing and Government Island embankment were designed by ODOT. The project was constructed under six contracts, with the majority of the sub- and superstructure work awarded to Willamette-Western Corp. (a division of Riedel International), Alaska Constructors, General Construction Co., S. J. Groves and Sons Co., Guy F. Atkinson Co., and Peter Kiewit Sons' Co.

Unusual Note—To celebrate the kickoff of National Transportation Week, 15 May 1983 was declared Columbia Crossing '83, and the Glenn Jackson Bridge was the star of the show. The result of a full year of planning by Oregon and Washington, the Columbia Crossing was the biggest celebration on a bridge in Portland's oft-celebrated bridge history. More than 200,000 people watched or participated in the world-class twelve-kilometer "Run between the States." Other day-long activities included hot-air balloon rides, square dance exhibitions, a bicycle crossing, boat parade, and dozens of concerts.

Approaches—North end (Washington): I-205, Washington State Highway 14. South end (Oregon): I-205. This enormous two-mile, eight-lane bridge vaults from the level of the Columbia River levee (low enough not to obstruct the flight path for Portland International Airport, immediately west of the bridge) to a height of nearly 144 feet to clear the 300-foot-wide ship channel.

The Jackson is part of I-205, a federally designated route that turns east from I-5 at Tualatin, Oregon, slips through east

Bicyclists and pedestrians are allowed on 12 Portland-area bridges, including the Glenn Jackson.

Portland (avoiding the downtown area), crosses the Columbia River into Washington, and connects with I-5 north of Vancouver. This transportation corridor is nearly 40 miles long.

Neighborhood/Landmarks—Racing along the Glenn Jackson Bridge, few motorists realize that the bridge passes through as remote and pastoral a spot to be found in any metropolitan area—1,760-acre Government Island, one of the largest river islands in the country. Despite its proximity

to two large cities, the island is accessible only by boat. It is known for its great blue heron colony and is popular with anglers. The interior, off limits to the public, contains a seasonal cattle ranch and protected natural area. Many threatened or endangered wildlife species live here, including Columbia white-tailed deer. Most of the island is owned by the Port of Portland, which operates Portland International Airport. According to *Oregon Geographic Names*, explorers Lewis and Clark visited the island in 1805.

RAILROAD BRIDGES

Columbia River
  BNSF Railway Bridge 9.6

Oregon Slough
  BNSF Railway Bridge 8.8

Willamette River
  BNSF Railway Bridge 5.1
  Union Pacific Railroad Bridge at Lake Oswego

Portland's Union Railroad Depot prior to 1913 and the Broadway Bridge.

WHILE THE EMPHASIS in this book is on highway bridges, there are several other river spans that have proved essential to the greater Portland area. There are four river bridges—one across the Columbia, one across the Oregon Slough, and two across the Willamette—that are used exclusively for railroad traffic. They are little known and largely ignored by an automobile-oriented society.

On the Columbia, just downriver from the Interstate Bridge at river mile 106.5, is the BNSF (Burlington Northern Santa Fe) Railway Bridge 9.6. A good spot to see this giant (467-foot swing span) in action is the Vancouver Amtrak Station. South of Bridge 9.6 on the BNSF line is Bridge 8.8 across the Oregon Slough. At river mile 7 on the Willamette, one mile upstream from the St. Johns Bridge, is BNSF Railway Bridge 5.1, one of the tallest and longest lift spans in the world. Thirteen miles farther up the Willamette, joining Lake Oswego and Milwaukie at river mile 20, is the railroad bridge acquired by Union Pacific Railroad in 1996 when it bought the Southern Pacific.

The Northern Pacific Railroad built BNSF Railway bridges 9.6, 8.8, and 5.1 for the Spokane, Portland, and Seattle Railway Co. during Theodore Roosevelt's administration in 1908-1909. These three bridges, named for their miles from Portland's Union Station, provide the main rail connection between Oregon and Washington. Ralph Modjeski designed all three (see Broadway Bridge and glossary).

Bridge 5.1 is known by different names, for example, Bridge 5.1, St. Johns Railroad Bridge, the Willamette River Bridge, and the Burlington Northern Railway Bridge, for its present owner.

The U.S. Coast Guard, under the jurisdiction of the Department of Transportation, is the regulator of bridges over navigable waters of the United States. If a bridge is an obstruction to river traffic, and a study shows that the benefits derived from replacement or repair of that obstruction are at least equal to the cost, then under the Truman

BNSF Bridge 9.6.

BNSF 5.1 as a swing span.

BNSF Railway Bridge 9.6 across the Columbia River.

Hobbs Act of 1945, money can be appropriated for the work. Bridge 5.1 is one such structure. During Ronald Reagan's administration, Congress authorized $38 million for reconstruction of Bridge 5.1, proved to be an impediment to navigation into Portland and upstream Willamette basins.

The bridge's swing span (1908), the longest in the world, was replaced in a two-year project ending in 1989. A 516-foot-long lift span, with a lift load of eight million pounds, was successfully put into place within the 72-hour maximum time limit. The present lift span is one of the highest in the world. Bridge 5.1, when open, provides total clearance at

BNSF Bridge 5.1 as a vertical lift bridge.

The Southern Pacific Railroad Bridge between Milwaukie and Lake Oswego is now owned by Union Pacific.

low water of 200 feet, which is higher than the clearance from low water to the bottom deck of the Fremont Bridge.

The design of the new towers and lift span is clean and compatible. The new structure is made of "weathering" steel and is rusting to a fine dark brown, as it was designed to do. The remaining fixed spans of the original bridge are painted silver. Since there is no way the

soft brown finish of the weathering steel can be duplicated in paint, the bridge, say some citizens, is an incongruous combination of materials and colors greeting every visitor who arrives by water. HNTB Engineering, designers of the new RiverWalk pedestrian and bicycle sidewalk on Steel Bridge, and the new Alsea Bay Bridge at Waldport, Oregon, designed Bridge 5.1's new lift span. HNTB was one of the successor firms of Waddell

& Harrington. (See Hawthorne and Steel bridges.) The Riedel and Tokola companies of Portland, a joint venture, won 5.1's lift span construction contract.

The Railroad Bridge at Lake Oswego—

In the early part of the century, government plans for Portland did not include the presence of steam freight and passenger trains on downtown streets. The Southern Pacific

123

Railroad Co., responding to the wishes of city planners for an eastside bypass, built track that included a bridge across the Willamette at river mile 20, between Lake Oswego and Milwaukie. Opened in 1910, the 1,378-foot bridge has been operated by Union Pacific since 1996, when UP acquired Southern Pacific. Its original railroad-designated name was "Willamette Structure 743.27," for its milepost distance from San Francisco, SP's former headquarters.

The bridge's Oswego side (west end) has a 50-foot steel approach span (deck plate girder), which was built in 1900 by the Phoenix Bridge Co. and installed elsewhere. It was moved to its current site in 1931, according to Southern Pacific records. Also on the Oswego side is a 60-foot open-deck trestle built in 1934. Two through truss spans (pin-connected) built in 1910, approximately 298 feet in length, hold the bridge's railway deck. On the Milwaukie side (east end) is a 668-foot open-deck trestle built in 1927.

On the west side, the bridge can be viewed from the new Foothills Park, opened in 2006 by the City of Lake Oswego. The best view, however, may be found in Milwaukie near the Oak Lodge Sanitary District property.

HOW AND WHY BRIDGES ARE BUILT by Ed Wortman

St. Johns Bridge in the process of construction with ferry landing to right at turn of the 20th century.

THERE ARE THREE MAIN STEPS in building a bridge: planning, design, and construction. As examples of these steps, references are made below to the new Sauvie Island Bridge, which is under construction while this chapter is being written. Please see the glossary for explanations of some of the technical terms used.

Each main step, or phase, in building a bridge can take from a few months to two or three years or more, depending on how big and how complicated the bridge. For example, building the new Sauvie Island Bridge requires about eight years from the start of planning to the end of construction.

125

Bridges normally are built and owned by public agencies such as cities, counties, and states, or by private companies such as railroads. In the case of Sauvie Island, the owner is Multnomah County, acting on behalf of citizens who ultimately "own" the bridge. The planning, design, and construction of a bridge usually is done by people working for the owner plus outside companies hired for specific parts of the project. Multnomah County planned and designed the new Sauvie Island Bridge with its primary engineering consultant, David Evans & Associates of Portland and Salem, Oregon. Several subconsultants also participated.

Planning

The planning team for a typical bridge project consists of engineers, transportation planners, land use planners, biologists, public officials, community representatives, and others. During the planning phase, this team must answer a number of questions, among them:

- What traffic will use the bridge?

  - How many cars, trucks, and buses will cross the bridge each day?
  - How many walkers, bicycles, and other users will use the bridge?
  - How many traffic lanes, bike lanes, and sidewalks will the bridge need?
  - Might the bridge have to carry other types of traffic now or in the future, such as streetcars or light rail?

- What are possible sites (general locations) for the bridge?

- For each possible site:

  - What is now on the site, such as rivers, wetlands, highways, houses, factories, etc.?
  - What effects would a bridge at this site have on the natural environment, trees, plants, fish, birds, other animals, water quality, air quality, etc.?
  - What effects would the bridge have on the human environment, including homes, businesses, recreation areas, neighborhood traffic, etc.?
  - How would the bridge connect to existing streets, highways, sidewalks, and bike routes? For example, how much new roadway would be needed at each end of the bridge?
  - How much property (land and buildings) would have to be bought to clear a path (the "right-of-way") for the bridge?

New Sauvie Island Bridge in construction with existing bridge in background.

- How would the site affect travel distances for bridge users?
- If the bridge would cross a waterway, what types of vessels use the waterway, such as ocean-going ships, tugboats, barges, sailboats?
- Would the bridge be high enough above the water to allow vessels to pass underneath, or would part of the bridge need to open to let them through?
- What other conditions at the site would affect the cost of the bridge, such as water depth, and type of ground?
- How much would the bridge cost? (At this point in the project, the cost figure would be an approximate "budget estimate.")
- How long would it take to design and build the bridge?

• Which of the possible sites do community groups prefer?

• Considering all the items above, what is the best site for the bridge?

• Where will the money (funding) come from to build the bridge? Possible sources of funding are:
  - Taxes on gasoline and other fuels
  - Tolls on bridge users
  - Sale of bonds, which must be paid off later from taxes or tolls

During planning for the new Sauvie Island Bridge, the planning team studied seven possible sites. The final choice was to build the new bridge alongside the existing bridge to the island. This site was chosen over the other possible sites because the cost will be lower, impacts on the natural environment will be smaller, and travel distance between the Portland area and the island is not increased.

Design

Members of the bridge design team include various types of engineers (civil, structural, electrical, transportation), as well as architects, public officials, and community representatives. The design phase consists of two parts: preliminary design and final design.

Preliminary Design – Questions to be answered during preliminary design include:

• If the bridge will cross a river, creek, or other waterway, how deep is the water, and how fast does it flow at different times?

• What are ground conditions at the site, such as type of soil and depth of soil to rock?

• How will the ground move in earthquakes?

• Are there any historical features or archeological relics (fossils, artifacts, and monuments of past human life and activities) at the site?

• Are there any existing utilities on, over, or under the site, such as electrical power lines, water pipes, fiber optic cables, etc.?

• Will the bridge carry utilities such as water pipes or natural gas lines?

• How much vertical (up and down) clearance will the bridge need over streets, highways, or waterways under the bridge?

• How much horizontal (sideways) clearance will be needed between bridge supports for streets, highways, waterways, or other facilities under the bridge?

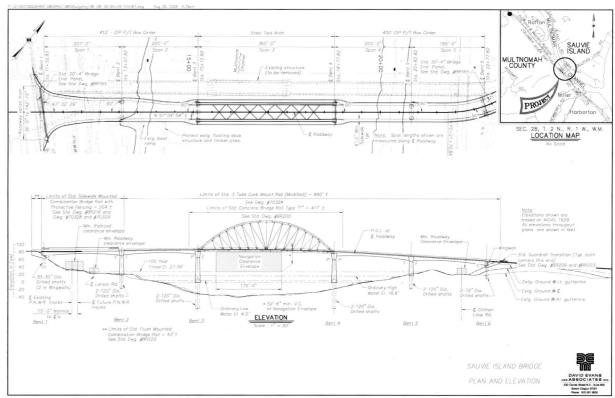

Plan and elevation drawing for 2008 Sauvie Island Bridge.

- What are possible arrangements of bridge supports and spans? In other words, how many supports could be used and how long would the bridge spans be between supports?

- What types of bridge structures could be used, such as concrete girders, steel girders, concrete arches, steel arches, steel trusses, cable-stayed spans, or suspension spans?

- If a movable span is needed, what type will be used: bascule, vertical lift, or swing?

- Do community groups have preferences as to the type of bridge and its appearance?

- Will architectural features be included to enhance the bridge's appearance?

- What measures will be needed during and after construction of the bridge to protect the natural environment from damage or pollution?

- What permits for building the bridge will be needed from public agencies such as the U.S. Army Corps of Engineers, U.S. Coast Guard, U.S. National Marine Fisheries Service, Department of State Lands, local land use planning agency, and others?

- Based on the preliminary design, about how much is the bridge expected to cost?

During preliminary design, decisions are made regarding:

- Exact location of the bridge

- Width of the bridge needed for traffic lanes, roadway shoulders, and sidewalks

- Number and location of bridge supports

- Length of spans between supports

- Vertical and horizontal clearances under the bridge

- Type of structure for each span

- Type of movable span, if needed

- Types of foundations in the ground, both on land and in water

- Architectural input on shapes and colors of the overall bridge and its parts.

During preliminary design, the project team also will start working to obtain funding for the bridge, to buy property needed for the bridge right-of-way, and to acquire necessary permits and approvals. On the new Sauvie Island Bridge project, at least 16 permits and approvals were required from 11 public agencies.

For the Sauvie Island Bridge, the design team decided to provide two 12-foot traffic lanes, two six-foot roadway shoulders, and two six-foot sidewalks (the shoulders are available for use by bicycles). Part of the bridge has a third traffic lane to avoid back-ups at the intersection with Highway 30 on the mainland. The main span over the river channel is a 360-foot long steel arch. This structure type was selected to give travelers the feeling of a "gateway" as they pass over the bridge, similar to the through truss main span in the old bridge. The new bridge also has two 200-foot long concrete box girder approach spans at each end. Foundations under the bridge support bents are drilled shafts, consisting of large steel pipes drilled down to bedrock and filled with concrete.

For the new Sauvie Island Bridge, funding comes from a combination of county, state, and federal sources.

Final Design: During the final design phase, the design team does the following:

- Calculates loads on the bridge from the bridge's own weight and the weight of traffic plus natural forces including wind, earthquakes, and water flow.

- Decides what type and strength material to use for each part of the bridge structure. On the Sauvie Island Bridge, weathering steel was chosen for the main span arch to reduce the amount of painting required at the time of construction and in the future.

- Decides how big and how strong each part must be. For example, designers of the Sauvie Island Bridge determined that the drilled shafts used as foundations for the main support bents must be ten feet in diameter. Shafts at Sauvie Island's end abutments are smaller.

- Decides the exact shape and size of every part of the bridge. For Sauvie Island Bridge, architects helped select the shapes and colors of all parts of the bridge. The concrete will be painted tan to complement the dark brown of the steel in the main span arch.

- Makes drawings, called plans, showing each part of the bridge as well as the finished bridge. For Sauvie Island, the final set of plans includes about 300 drawings showing everything from size of bolts to the length of the bridge—the little picture to the big picture.

- Writes specifications that give instructions for building the bridge, including types of materials to use, tests to be done, regulations to follow, etc. There are 430 pages in Sauvie Island's book of specifications.

- Estimates the final cost for building the bridge based on the cost of materials, labor, equipment, and other expenses.

- Develops a construction schedule showing how long the project will take. For the new Sauvie Island Bridge, the owner's schedule estimated that the bridge could be built in about three years.

- Writes other documents to use in hiring a contractor to build the bridge.

Construction

As the first step in the construction phase for a bridge, the owner hires a general contractor to carry out the actual construction work. The general contractor usually does some of the work with its own crews and hires subcontractors to do other work.

The usual method for hiring a general contractor is as follows:

1. Prepare final plans and specifications as described above.

2. Advertise for general contractors to submit bids to do the work. For the new Sauvie Island Bridge, five contractors submitted bids. The five bids ranged from a low of about $38 million to a high of $48 million.

3. Award a contract to the low bidder. The contract for the new Sauvie Island Bridge was awarded to the low bidder, Max J. Kuney Company of Spokane, Washington, in late 2005.

Once the owner awards the general contract, the selected contractor becomes responsible for actually building the bridge. From then on, the owner's main jobs are to assure that the work is done properly and to pay the contractor for work accomplished each month.

Two key tasks to be performed by the general contractor at the beginning of the project are to:

- Plan the overall project. This includes developing a detailed schedule to show when all the various activities will be done in relation to each other. For the new Sauvie Island Bridge, the general contractor's schedule lists about 300 different activities.

- Hire subcontractors to carry out portions of the on-site work. At Sauvie Island, subcontractors were hired for a number of tasks, such as surveying, strengthening ground under the bridge, installing drilled shafts, building an approach roadway embankment on the island out of crushed rock, paving the embankment roadway, assembling and erecting the steel arch, installing electrical systems, demolishing the old bridge, and landscaping. The general contractor's own crews are building temporary work bridges in the river, a temporary detour bridge, concrete support bents, concrete approach girders, and the concrete deck and sidewalks on the arch span.

Once the subcontractors are selected, it is up to all contractors (general and subs) to plan and carry out their specific parts of the work. To do this, each contractor must:

- Develop a schedule for work to fit within the general contractor's overall schedule.

- Buy temporary and permanent materials needed for each part of the work. Sauvie Island Bridge's temporary materials include steel piling and wood for concrete forms. Permanent materials include crushed rock, concrete, steel casings for drilled shafts, reinforcing steel for concrete, structural steel parts, drain piping, and electrical wiring. On Sauvie Island, the general contractor is buying parts for the steel arch from Fought & Company, a Portland-area steel fabricator.

- Decide what methods and equipment to use for each part of the work.

- Supply the equipment, either from its own equipment fleet or from a rental company.

- Hire crews of craftspeople to do the work. On the Sauvie Island project, craftspeople include pilebucks, carpenters, laborers, cement masons, operating engineers (equipment operators), reinforcing steel ironworkers, structural ironworkers, surveyors, and electricians.

- Manage and direct the work. For the general contractor, this means managing the subcontractors as well as the general contractor's own crews.

- Provide quality control (QC) for the work. On the Sauvie Island project, outside inspection companies are hired to perform QC tasks such as checking crushed rock fill to make sure it is tightly-compacted, making and testing concrete samples, testing for empty spaces in drilled shaft concrete, inspecting welds in steel components, and checking sizes and locations of all parts of the project.

Many of the general methods used to build bridges are hundreds, even thousands, of years old. Details of the methods vary from year to year and from project to project. When planning a particular bridge project, each contractor or subcontractor chooses what methods and equipment to use depending on such factors as physical requirements of the work, site conditions, contractual requirements in the plans and specifications, available technology, the contractor's experience, equipment owned by the contractor, and, of course, cost. Cost is generally the overriding reason for deciding how to do the work. In order to make the project a business success, the contractor's goal is to perform the work for the minimum cost while meeting requirements for safety, quality, environmental protection, and schedule.

Following are some of the methods and equipment used by the contractors on the new Sauvie Island Bridge for various parts of the project:

- **Drilled Shaft Foundations:** For each shaft, a large steel casing pipe is stood on end by a crawler crane and installed deep into the ground by an "oscillator" tool that twists and pushes the casing down. The crane digs the loose dirt out of the casing with a clamshell-type bucket. When the casing reaches solid rock, the crane lowers a tool inside to cut a socket into the rock. The crane then places a cage of steel reinforcing bars inside the casing and socket. Finally, concrete is pumped into the casing to make a solid column to support the bridge.

- Concrete Box Girders: At Sauvie Island, the contractor is building two 200-foot long prestressed concrete box girder approach spans at each end of the new bridge. The top slab of the box girders serves as the roadway deck for the bridge. The girders are supported by concrete abutments and bents that are, in turn, supported by drilled shafts. For some bridges, concrete girders are built off-site ("precast"), then trucked to the site and lifted into final position with large cranes. However, for the new Sauvie Island Bridge, the concrete girders are "cast-in-place" rather than precast due to their large size and complicated shapes. For cast-in-place girders the contractor first builds a system of temporary supports called "falsework." The forms for holding the concrete are then assembled on the falsework. Next, concrete is pumped into the forms and allowed to harden. The final step in building the girders is to pull steel wires through plastic tubes in the concrete, then post-tension the wires by pulling on them with jacks. (See prestressed concrete in the glossary.) After the girders are finished, the contractor removes the forms and falsework, leaving the girders supported by the abutments and bents.

- Steel Arch: The main span of the Sauvie Island Bridge over the Multnomah Channel is a 360-foot long steel tied arch. The arch is supported on concrete piers at both sides of the channel. The arch structure consists of: (a) a box-shaped steel arch rib on each side of the roadway, (b) steel box tie girders serving as tension ties between the ends of the arch ribs, (c) steel suspender cables carrying the weight of the tie girders and roadway to the arch, (d) steel floorbeams spanning crossways between the two tie girders, (e) steel stringers spanning lengthwise between the floorbeams, (f) a concrete roadway deck on the stringers, (g) concrete sidewalks supported on steel floorbeams and stringers outside the tie girders. There are three

Building drilled shaft foundations for new Sauvie Island Bridge, 2006.

standard ways to build a tied arch bridge: assemble it in place on temporary falsework, assemble it in place using a temporary support system similar to a cable-stayed bridge, or assemble it away from the bridge site and float it into place. For the Sauvie Island project, the owner did not allow the first method—using falsework in the river channel—because of environmental impacts and interference with boat traffic. Of the two remaining options, the contractor chose the third one, referred to as the "float-in" method. Following is the contractor's process for building and installing the arch.

1. Make the steel parts at Fought and other fabricating plants.

2. Ship the parts on trucks to an assembly site on a dock by the Willamette River in Northwest Portland.

3. Assemble the span on temporary supports on the dock. Connect the parts together with high-strength bolts.

4. Slide and roll the finished span from the dock onto a barge.

5. Lift the span with hydraulic jacks on jacking towers on the barge until the span is high enough to fit over the piers at the bridge site.

6. Tow the barge with the span to the bridge site with tugboats.

7. Move the barge into position with the span lined up over the piers.

Building approach embankment for new Sauvie Island Bridge, 2006.

8. Lower the barge by pumping water into it until the span lands on the piers.

9. Remove the barge and all temporary equipment.

10. Place the concrete deck and sidewalks on the steel structure.

- **Approach Embankment on Island:** The approach embankment at the island end of the new bridge is 1,000 feet long and about 35 feet high where it meets the bridge. The embankment is made of crushed rock fill with pieces of rock up to six inches wide. About 4,000 truckloads of rocks were hauled to the island from a nearby quarry on the mainland. After each truckload, a bulldozer pushed and leveled the pile into a one-foot thick layer. A heavy roller then drove back and forth over the new fill to squeeze ("compact") the rocks tightly together. The finished embankment consists of as many as 35 one-foot layers of rock fill.

- **Other Construction Work:** In addition to the major activities described above, other work on the Sauvie Island Bridge project includes installation or construction of the following:

  - Railings along the outside edges of the sidewalks

  - Drain pipes and treatment facilities for rain water collected from the bridge deck

  - Electric lights in the box girders for maintenance crews

  - Asphalt pavement on the approach embankment

  - Traffic lane stripes on the bridge deck and embankment pavement

  - Traffic signals at the Highway 30 intersection at the mainland end of the bridge

  - Parking lot and bus turnaround at the island end of the bridge.

Why Bridges Are Built

Bridges are built for various reasons—nine reasons are listed below. The list refers to existing and past bridges in the Portland area and shows the year when each bridge opened. Some are listed more than once since there can be several reasons for building a particular bridge:

1. To replace ferry boats. Examples: First Interstate (I-5) Bridge (1917); Sellwood Bridge (1925); St. Johns Bridge (1931); Sauvie Island Bridge (1950). Also, the original Morrison Bridge (1887), no longer standing.

2. To connect existing streets where there is no crossing. Examples: Broadway Bridge (1913); Ross Island Bridge (1926).

3. To carry new highways or railroad lines. Examples: Most of the freeway bridges in the Portland area, including Marquam (1966), Abernethy (1970), Fremont (1973), and Glenn Jackson (1982). Also railroad bridges such as BNSF Railway Bridges 5.1, 8.8, and 9.6 (all 1908), and Union Pacific Railroad Bridge at Lake Oswego (1910).

4. To increase traffic capacity of existing highways. Example: Second Interstate (I-5) Bridge (1958).

5. To replace bridges that are too small or are worn out from traffic. Examples: Hawthorne Bridge (1910); Steel Bridge (1912); Oregon City Bridge (1922); Burnside Bridge (1926); Morrison Bridge (1958); Bybee Boulevard Bridge over McLoughlin Boulevard (2004); new Sauvie Island Bridge (2008).

6. To carry streets, highways, or bicycle/pedestrian trails over railroad tracks, cross-streets, or other obstructions to traffic. Examples: overpasses over I-5, I-84, I-205, and I-405 freeways, as well as Highways 26 and 217; new bridges over railroad tracks in Albina Industrial District and St. Johns; new bicycle/pedestrian bridges on Springwater Corridor Trail.

7. To improve access for ships passing through existing bridges. Example: Replacement of old swing span with new lift span at BNSF Railway Bridge 5.1 (1989). This was one of the reasons for replacement of the earlier Burnside (1894), Morrison (1905), and Steel (1888) bridges, also swing spans.

8. To replace bridges damaged or destroyed by fires, ship impacts, earthquakes, wars, or other events. None of the existing bridges in the Portland area were built primarily for this reason. However, bridges in other parts of the U.S. and the world are replaced every year due to damage or loss from natural or human-caused events. In Portland, Madison Bridge No. 1 (1891) at the site of the Hawthorne Bridge was damaged by fire and replaced by Madison Bridge No. 2 in 1900.

9. To replace bridges that are vulnerable to collapse or damage in earthquakes. This has not been a primary reason for building any new bridges in the Portland area. However, the possibility of damage in future earthquakes has been a consideration in deciding whether to replace the Sauvie Island and Sellwood bridges.

The 1888 Steel Bridge was replaced in1912 in favor of a new lift span, allowing faster ship passage.

APPENDICES

WILLAMETTE RIVER BRIDGES
Portland, Oregon

This image shows the city loop formed by the Interstate 5 and 405 freeways. The Fremont Bridge which will complete the loop is under construction (far right.) Courtesy of Oregon Department of Transportation, 1972.

Portland's ten Willamette River vehicular bridges began as solutions to the problem of linking the city's residential east side with its west side business center. They also reflected the powerful economic influences of real estate developers, street railway companies, and railroads. By the 1920s, common use of the auto motivated the building of new bridges to handle more traffic and serve outlying areas such as Sellwood and St. Johns. After World War II, older bridges received new approaches and ramps to further speed commuter traffic and link it to the new state highways. Starting in the 1960s, new spans in the emerging freeway system helped maintain the flow of through traffic and reduce downtown congestion. Leading American civil engineers such as J.A.L. Waddell, John Lyle Harrington, Ralph Modjeski, Ira Hedrick, Gustav Lindenthal, and David Steinman, found that work designing Portland's big bridges challenged them to develop innovative solutions, some later applied nationally.

Five Portland bridges accommodate river traffic either by lifting vertically or by having two leaves that swing upward to separate. The 1910 Hawthorne and the 1912 Steel are two of the nation's earliest vertical lift spans. Waddell & Harrington, the firm that created this technology, developed many of its essential features in Portland. The Steel Bridge has a railroad deck that lifts by telescoping into the upper deck, permitting the passage of small vessels, and an upper deck that also lifts to make way for large ships, a combination found nowhere else in the country. The largest of its type ever built, the 1913 Broadway Bridge opens using a rare Rall bascule mechanism that allows its two leaves to both lift and roll back.

Early movable spans had wooden decks, but by the 1920s engineers sought to reduce deck repair costs and make auto crossing safer. The 1926 Burnside Bridge pioneered the use of reinforced concrete on its bascule deck, an innovation that required powerful machinery to move its 10 million pounds of concrete and steel. By contrast, the 1958 Morrison was built with a steel grate bascule deck, a technology first used locally to replace the Hawthorne deck in 1945.

Although engineers had earlier proposed building high bridges, the 1925 Sellwood and the 1926 Ross Island were the first to span the river high enough to allow river traffic to pass. The Sellwood employs a rare four-span continuous truss to do so, while the Ross Island embodies Gustav Lindenthal's wide-ranging creativity as he tailored a cantilever span to fit within serious topographic and financial constraints. The tight budget was one legacy of local 1920s bridge contract scandals that Lindenthal also helped resolve. In 1931, the much better financed St. Johns created a high crossing by using suspension technology. A common solution nationally, but one rare in Oregon.

In contrast to the St. Johns, whose Gothic arches have earned it acclaim for its beauty, the 1966 Marquam evoked formal protest from the Portland Arts Commission. Engineers saw, instead, an economical truss design carrying a double-deck expressway more than 1,000 feet across the river. Engineers for the 1973 Fremont also displayed technological sophistication, including extensive computer use, but the Marquam experience prompted vocal public participation in the Fremont's design. The elegant three-span tied arch that resulted is both the world's longest and an unusual American case of a type more common in Europe.

Portland's bridges also required innovative construction methods. Despite its novel weight-saving orthotropic deck and use of the latest high-strength steel, the Fremont's 6,000 ton center span challenged the relatively new erection techniques that had never previously lifted such weight. More than sixty years earlier, the 9 million pound total weight of the Steel Bridge's liftspan and counterweights, by far the heaviest yet, posed a comparable challenge. The local contractor built an elaborate wooden falsework between the bridge's fixed spans, erecting the lift decks and pouring the concrete main counterweights in place.

State Map of Oregon

Cut Line
Page 1 of 3

135

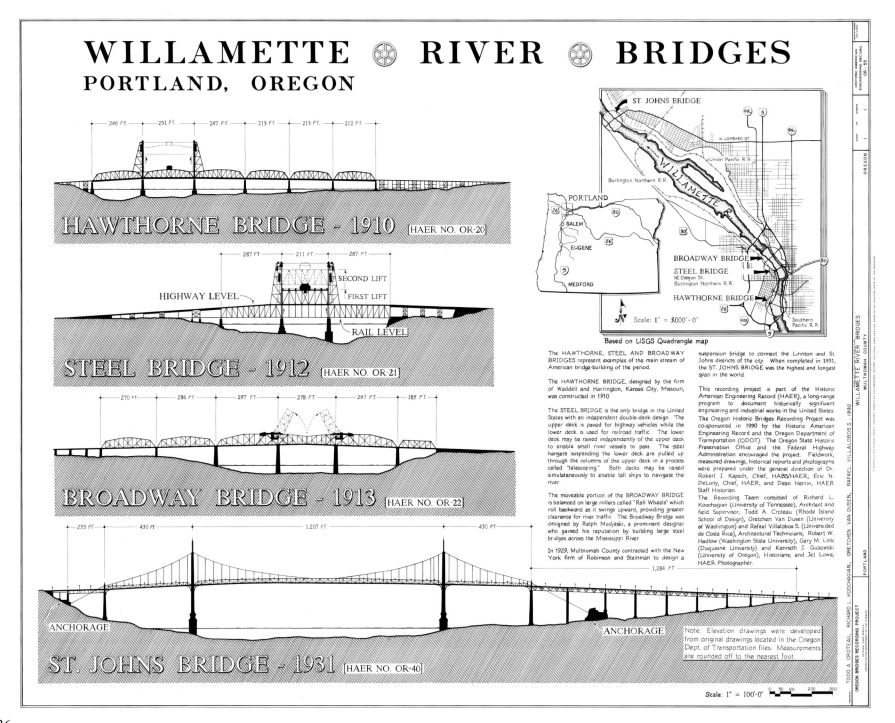

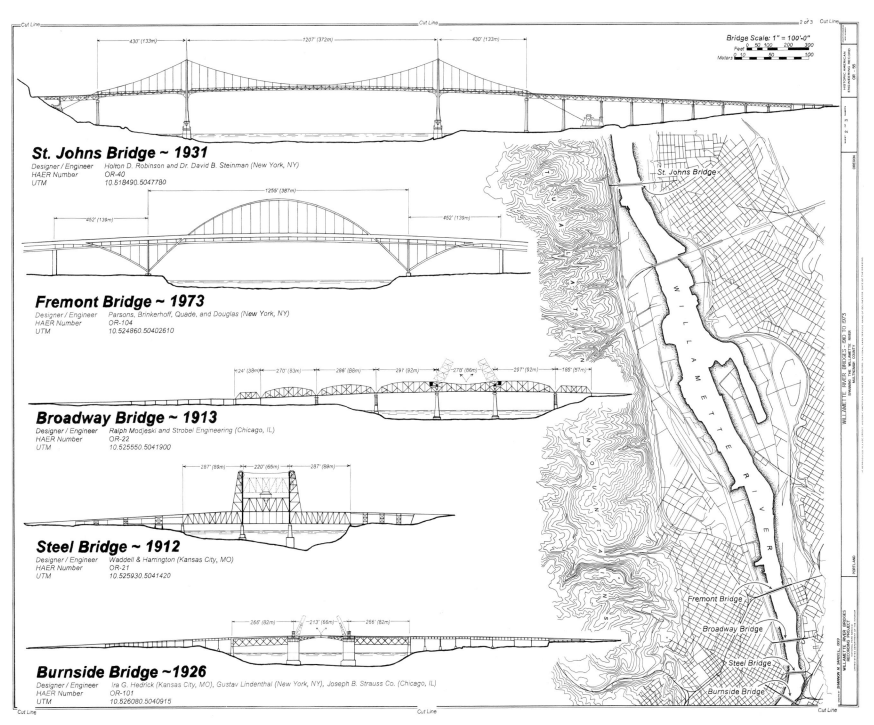

Bridge Scale: 1" = 100'-0"

430' (133m)   1207' (372m)   430' (133m)

St. Johns Bridge ~ 1931
Designer / Engineer   Holton D. Robinson and Dr. David B. Steinman (New York, NY)
HAER Number   OR-40
UTM   10.518490.5047780

1255' (387m)
452' (139m)   452' (139m)

Fremont Bridge ~ 1973
Designer / Engineer   Parsons, Brinkerhoff, Quade, and Douglas (New York, NY)
HAER Number   OR-104
UTM   10.524860.50402610

124' (38m) 270' (83m) 286' (88m) 297' (92m) 278' (86m) 297' (92m) 185' (57m)

Broadway Bridge ~ 1913
Designer / Engineer   Ralph Modjeski and Strobel Engineering (Chicago, IL)
HAER Number   OR-22
UTM   10.525550.5041900

287' (89m) 220' (65m) 287' (89m)

Steel Bridge ~ 1912
Designer / Engineer   Waddell & Harrington (Kansas City, MO)
HAER Number   OR-21
UTM   10.525930.5041420

266' (82m) 213' (66m) 266' (82m)

Burnside Bridge ~1926
Designer / Engineer   Ira G. Hedrick (Kansas City, MO), Gustav Lindenthal (New York, NY), Joseph B. Strauss Co. (Chicago, IL)
HAER Number   OR-101
UTM   10.526080.5040915

St. Johns Bridge

WILLAMETTE RIVER

Fremont Bridge

Broadway Bridge

Steel Bridge

Burnside Bridge

137

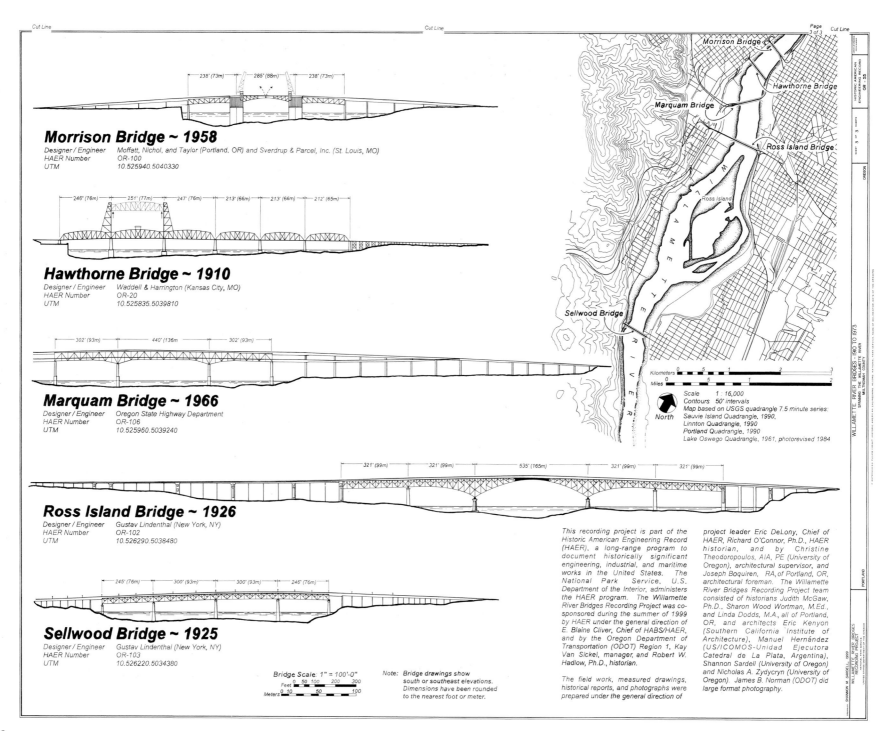

Morrison Bridge ~ 1958
Designer / Engineer   Moffatt, Nichol, and Taylor (Portland, OR) and Sverdrup & Parcel, Inc. (St. Louis, MO)
HAER Number   OR-100
UTM   10.525940.5040330

Hawthorne Bridge ~ 1910
Designer / Engineer   Waddell & Harrington (Kansas City, MO)
HAER Number   OR-20
UTM   10.525835.5039810

Marquam Bridge ~ 1966
Designer / Engineer   Oregon State Highway Department
HAER Number   OR-106
UTM   10.525960.5039240

Ross Island Bridge ~ 1926
Designer / Engineer   Gustav Lindenthal (New York, NY)
HAER Number   OR-102
UTM   10.526290.5038480

Sellwood Bridge ~ 1925
Designer / Engineer   Gustav Lindenthal (New York, NY)
HAER Number   OR-103
UTM   10.526220.5034380

Scale   1 : 16,000
Contours   50' intervals
Map based on USGS quadrangle 7.5 minute series:
Sauvie Island Quadrangle, 1990,
Linnton Quadrangle, 1990
Portland Quadrangle, 1990
Lake Oswego Quadrangle, 1961, photorevised 1984

Bridge Scale: 1" = 100'-0"

Note: Bridge drawings show
south or southeast elevations.
Dimensions have been rounded
to the nearest foot or meter.

This recording project is part of the Historic American Engineering Record (HAER), a long-range program to document historically significant engineering, industrial, and maritime works in the United States. The National Park Service, U.S. Department of the Interior, administers the HAER program. The Willamette River Bridges Recording Project was co-sponsored during the summer of 1999 by HAER under the general direction of E. Blaine Cliver, Chief of HABS/HAER, and by the Oregon Department of Transportation (ODOT) Region 1, Kay Van Sickel, manager, and Robert W. Hadlow, Ph.D., historian.

The field work, measured drawings, historical reports, and photographs were prepared under the general direction of project leader Eric DeLony, Chief of HAER, Richard O'Connor, Ph.D., HAER historian, and by Christine Theodoropoulos, AIA, PE (University of Oregon), architectural supervisor, and Joseph Boquiren, RA, of Portland, OR, architectural foreman. The Willamette River Bridges Recording Project team consisted of historians Judith McGaw, Ph.D., Sharon Wood Wortman, M.Ed., and Linda Dodds, M.A., all of Portland, OR, and architects Eric Kenyon (Southern California Institute of Architecture), Manuel Hernández (US/ICOMOS-Unidad Ejecutora Catedral de La Plata, Argentina), Shannon Sardell (University of Oregon) and Nicholas A. Zydycryn (University of Oregon). James B. Norman (ODOT) did large format photography.

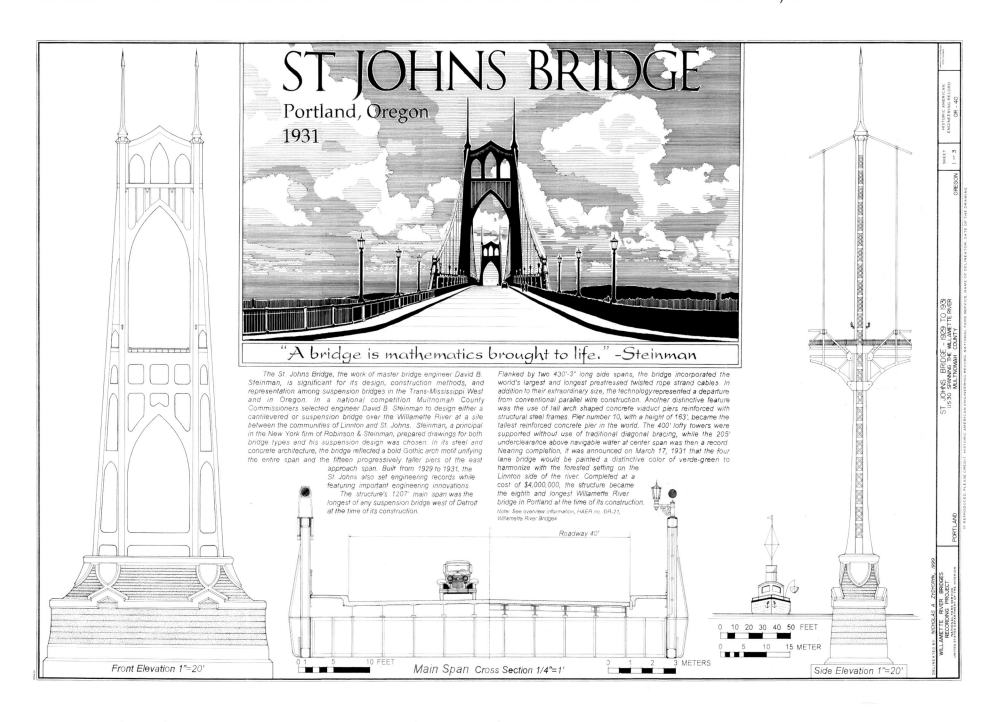

ST JOHNS BRIDGE
Portland, Oregon
1931

"A bridge is mathematics brought to life." -Steinman

The St. Johns Bridge, the work of master bridge engineer David B. Steinman, is significant for its design, construction methods, and representation among suspension bridges in the Trans-Mississippi West and in Oregon. In a national competition Multnomah County Commissioners selected engineer David B. Steinman to design either a cantilevered or suspension bridge over the Willamette River at a site between the communities of Linnton and St. Johns. Steinman, a principal in the New York firm of Robinson & Steinman, prepared drawings for both bridge types and his suspension design was chosen. In its steel and concrete architecture, the bridge reflected a bold Gothic arch motif unifying the entire span and the fifteen progressively taller piers of the east approach span. Built from 1929 to 1931, the St. Johns also set engineering records while featuring important engineering innovations.

The structure's 1207' main span was the longest of any suspension bridge west of Detroit at the time of its construction.

Flanked by two 430'-3" long side spans, the bridge incorporated the world's largest and longest prestressed twisted rope strand cables. In addition to their extraordinary size, the technology represented a departure from conventional parallel wire construction. Another distinctive feature was the use of tall arch shaped concrete viaduct piers reinforced with structural steel frames. Pier number 10, with a height of 163', became the tallest reinforced concrete pier in the world. The 400' lofty towers were supported without use of traditional diagonal bracing, while the 205' underclearance above navigable water at center span was then a record. Nearing completion, it was announced on March 17, 1931 that the four lane bridge would be painted a distinctive color of verde-green to harmonize with the forested setting on the Linnton side of the river. Completed at a cost of $4,000,000, the structure became the eighth and longest Willamette River bridge in Portland at the time of its construction.

Note: See overview information, HAER no. OR-21, Willamette River Bridges

Front Elevation 1"=20'

Roadway 40'

0 1   5   10 FEET

Main Span Cross Section 1/4"=1'

0   1   2   3 METERS

0 10 20 30 40 50 FEET

0   5   10   15 METER

Side Elevation 1"=20'

DELINEATED BY NICHOLAS A. ZYZYNN, 1999
WILLAMETTE RIVER BRIDGES RECORDING PROJECT
NATIONAL PARK SERVICE
UNITED STATES DEPARTMENT OF THE INTERIOR

PORTLAND

ST. JOHNS BRIDGE - 1929 TO 1931
SPANNING THE WILLAMETTE RIVER
US 30 MULTNOMAH COUNTY

HISTORIC AMERICAN ENGINEERING RECORD
OR - 40

OREGON

SHEET 1 OF 3

IF REPRODUCED PLEASE CREDIT: HISTORIC AMERICAN ENGINEERING RECORD, NATIONAL PARK SERVICE, NAME OF DELINEATOR, DATE OF THE DRAWING

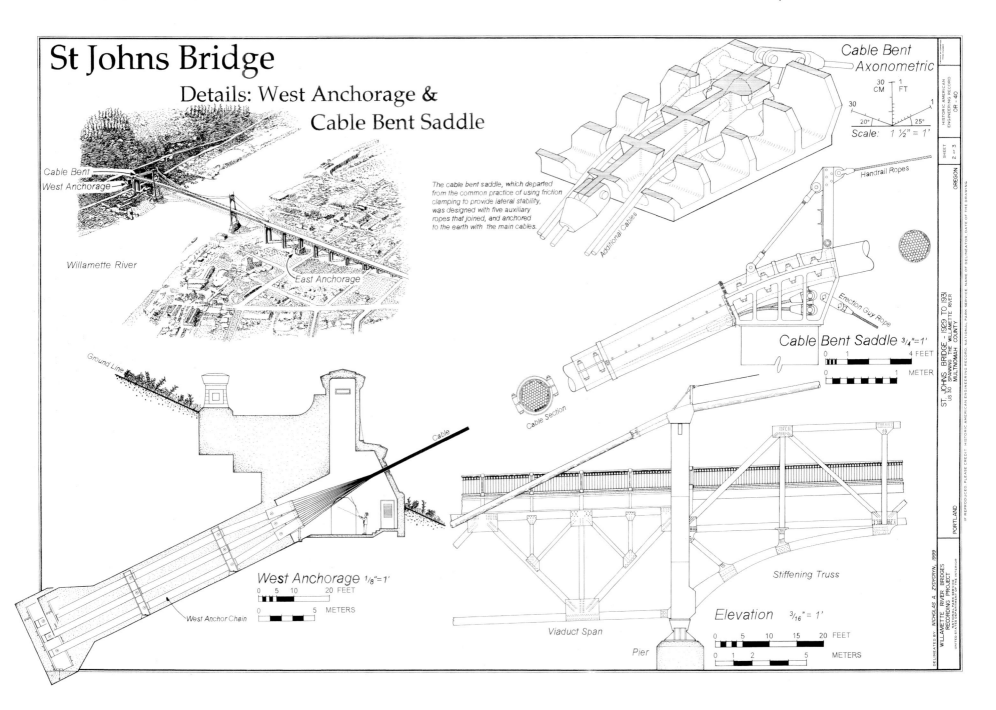

St Johns Bridge

Details: West Anchorage & Cable Bent Saddle

Cable Bent
Axonometric

Scale: 1 ½" = 1'

Cable Bent

West Anchorage

Willamette River

East Anchorage

The cable bent saddle, which departed from the common practice of using friction clamping to provide lateral stability, was designed with five auxiliary ropes that joined, and anchored to the earth with the main cables.

Additional Cables

Handrail Ropes

Erection Guy Rope

Cable Bent Saddle 3/4"=1'

Ground Line

Cable

Cable Section

West Anchorage 1/8"=1'

West Anchor Chain

Stiffening Truss

Elevation 3/16" = 1'

Viaduct Span

Pier

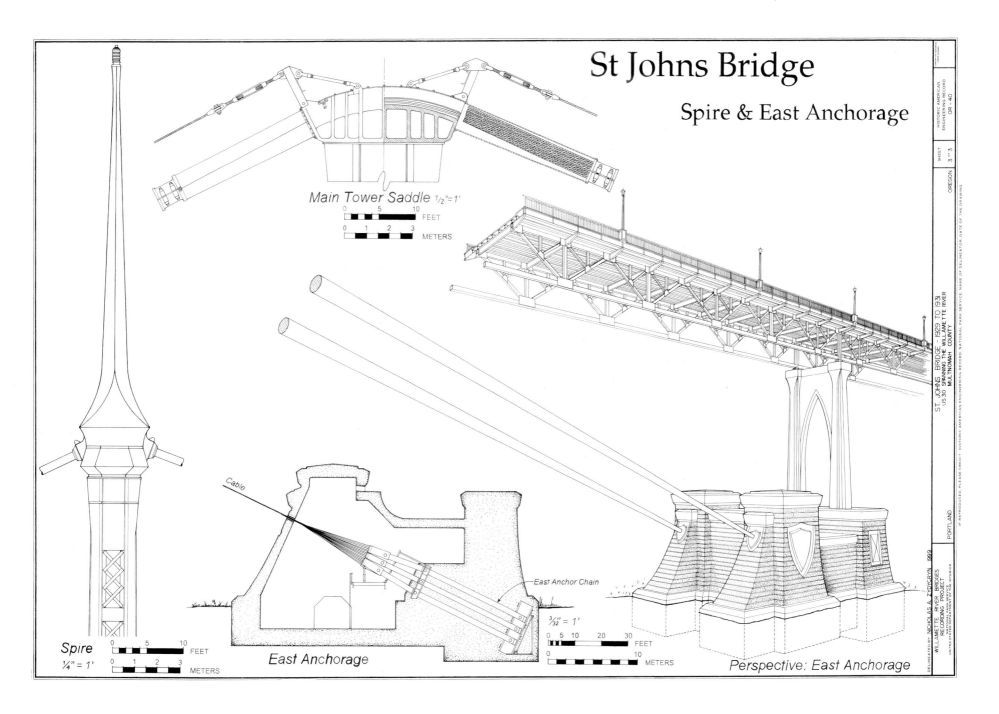

St Johns Bridge

Spire & East Anchorage

Main Tower Saddle 1/2"=1'

0 5 10 FEET

0 1 2 3 METERS

Cable

East Anchor Chain

3/32" = 1'

0 5 10   20   30 FEET

0   10 METERS

Spire

1/4" = 1'

0 5 10 FEET

0 1 2 3 METERS

East Anchorage

Perspective: East Anchorage

HISTORIC AMERICAN ENGINEERING RECORD OR - 40

SHEET 3 OF 3   OREGON

ST. JOHNS BRIDGE - 1929 TO 1931
US 30 SPANNING THE WILLAMETTE RIVER
MULTNOMAH COUNTY

PORTLAND

DELINEATED BY NICHOLAS A. ZYDGRYN, 1999
WILLAMETTE RIVER BRIDGES
RECORDING PROJECT

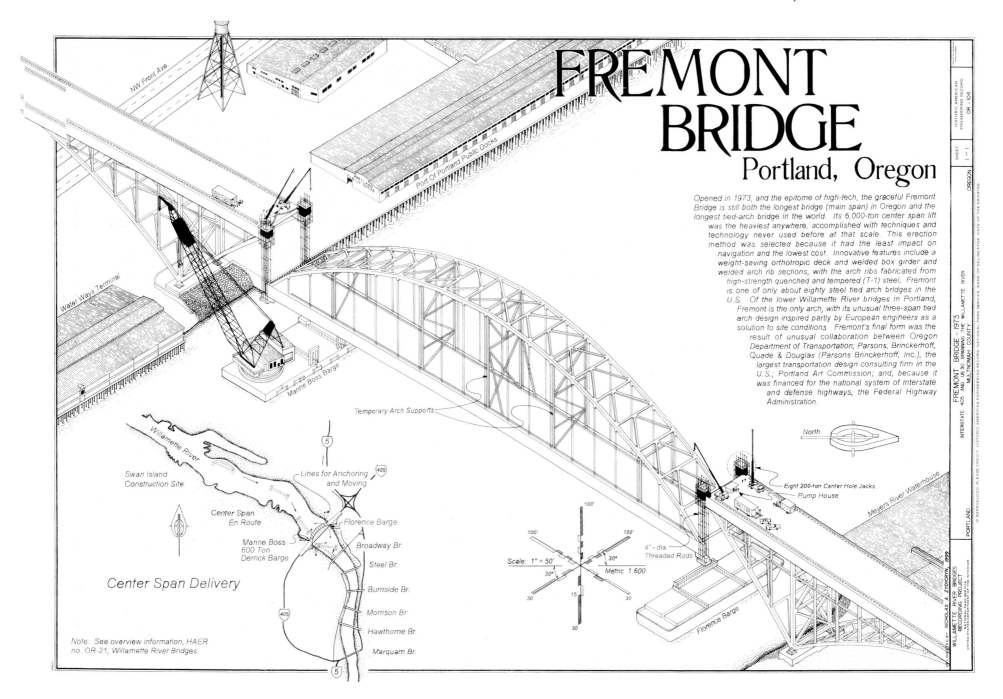

FREMONT BRIDGE
Portland, Oregon

Opened in 1973, and the epitome of high-tech, the graceful Fremont Bridge is still both the longest bridge (main span) in Oregon and the longest tied-arch bridge in the world. Its 6,000-ton center span lift was the heaviest anywhere, accomplished with techniques and technology never used before at that scale. This erection method was selected because it had the least impact on navigation and the lowest cost. Innovative features include a weight-saving orthotropic deck and welded box girder and welded arch rib sections, with the arch ribs fabricated from high-strength quenched and tempered (T-1) steel. Fremont is one of only about eighty steel tied arch bridges in the U.S. Of the lower Willamette River bridges in Portland, Fremont is the only arch, with its unusual three-span tied arch design inspired partly by European engineers as a solution to site conditions. Fremont's final form was the result of unusual collaboration between Oregon Department of Transportation; Parsons, Brinckerhoff, Quade & Douglas (Parsons Brinckerhoff, Inc.), the largest transportation design consulting firm in the U.S.; Portland Art Commission; and, because it was financed for the national system of interstate and defense highways, the Federal Highway Administration.

NW Front Ave.

Port Of Portland Public Docks

Water Ways Terminal

Marine Boss Barge

Temporary Arch Supports

North

Eight 200-ton Center Hole Jacks
Pump House

Meyers River Waterhouse

Willamette River

Swan Island Construction Site

Lines for Anchoring and Moving

Center Span En Route

Florence Barge

Marine Boss 600 Ton Derrick Barge

Broadway Br.

Steel Br.

Burnside Br.

Morrison Br.

Hawthorne Br.

Marquam Br.

Center Span Delivery

4" - dia. Threaded Rods

Scale: 1" = 50'

Metric 1:600

100'
100'
100'
100'
30°
30°
30
15
30
30

Florence Barge

Note: See overview information, HAER no. OR-21, Willamette River Bridges.

HISTORIC AMERICAN ENGINEERING RECORD
OR - 104
SHEET 1 OF 1
OREGON
FREMONT BRIDGE - 1973, SPANNING THE WILLAMETTE RIVER
INTERSTATE 405 AND US30
MULTNOMAH COUNTY
PORTLAND
DELINEATED BY: NICHOLAS A. ZYDYCRYN, 1999
WILLAMETTE RIVER BRIDGES RECORDING PROJECT
NATIONAL PARK SERVICE
UNITED STATES DEPARTMENT OF THE INTERIOR
IF REPRODUCED, PLEASE CREDIT: HISTORIC AMERICAN ENGINEERING RECORD, NATIONAL PARK SERVICE, NAME OF DELINEATOR, DATE OF THE DRAWING

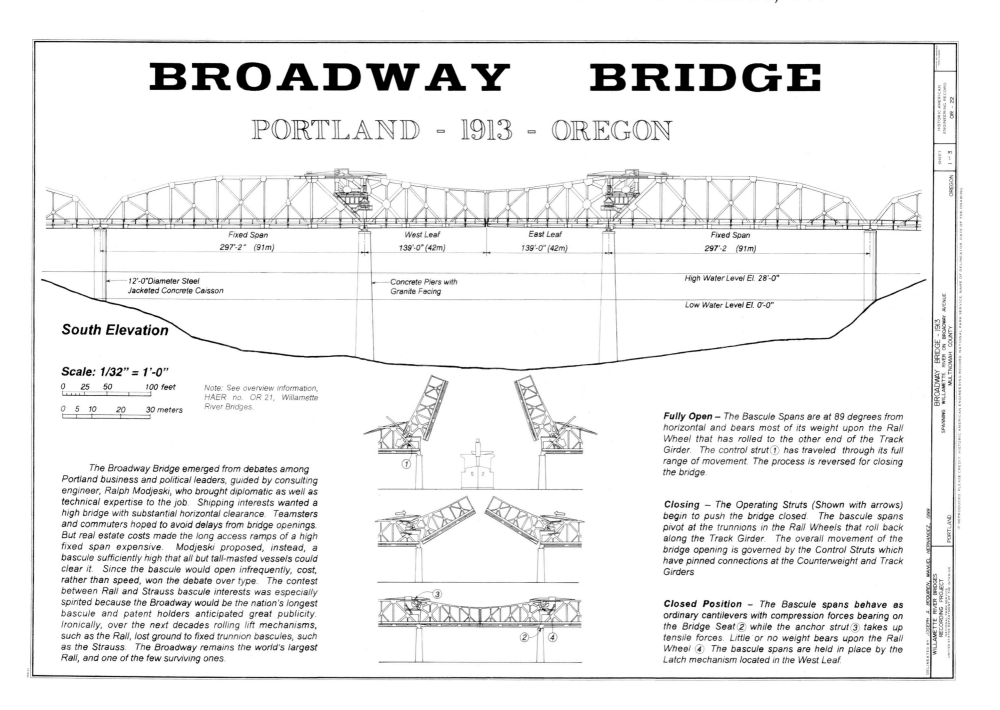

BROADWAY BRIDGE

PORTLAND - 1913 - OREGON

Fixed Span
297'-2" (91m)

West Leaf
139'-0" (42m)

East Leaf
139'-0" (42m)

Fixed Span
297'-2 (91m)

12'-0"Diameter Steel
Jacketed Concrete Caisson

Concrete Piers with
Granite Facing

High Water Level El. 28'-0"

Low Water Level El. 0'-0"

South Elevation

Scale: 1/32" = 1'-0"

0   25   50   100 feet

0   5   10   20   30 meters

Note: See overview information,
HAER no. OR 21, Willamette
River Bridges.

The Broadway Bridge emerged from debates among
Portland business and political leaders, guided by consulting
engineer, Ralph Modjeski, who brought diplomatic as well as
technical expertise to the job. Shipping interests wanted a
high bridge with substantial horizontal clearance. Teamsters
and commuters hoped to avoid delays from bridge openings.
But real estate costs made the long access ramps of a high
fixed span expensive. Modjeski proposed, instead, a
bascule sufficiently high that all but tall-masted vessels could
clear it. Since the bascule would open infrequently, cost,
rather than speed, won the debate over type. The contest
between Rall and Strauss bascule interests was especially
spirited because the Broadway would be the nation's longest
bascule and patent holders anticipated great publicity.
Ironically, over the next decades rolling lift mechanisms,
such as the Rall, lost ground to fixed trunnion bascules, such
as the Strauss. The Broadway remains the world's largest
Rall, and one of the few surviving ones.

Fully Open – The Bascule Spans are at 89 degrees from
horizontal and bears most of its weight upon the Rall
Wheel that has rolled to the other end of the Track
Girder. The control strut ① has traveled through its full
range of movement. The process is reversed for closing
the bridge.

Closing – The Operating Struts (Shown with arrows)
begin to push the bridge closed. The bascule spans
pivot at the trunnions in the Rall Wheels that roll back
along the Track Girder. The overall movement of the
bridge opening is governed by the Control Struts which
have pinned connections at the Counterweight and Track
Girders

Closed Position – The Bascule spans behave as
ordinary cantilevers with compression forces bearing on
the Bridge Seat ② while the anchor strut ③ takes up
tensile forces. Little or no weight bears upon the Rall
Wheel ④ The bascule spans are held in place by the
Latch mechanism located in the West Leaf.

143

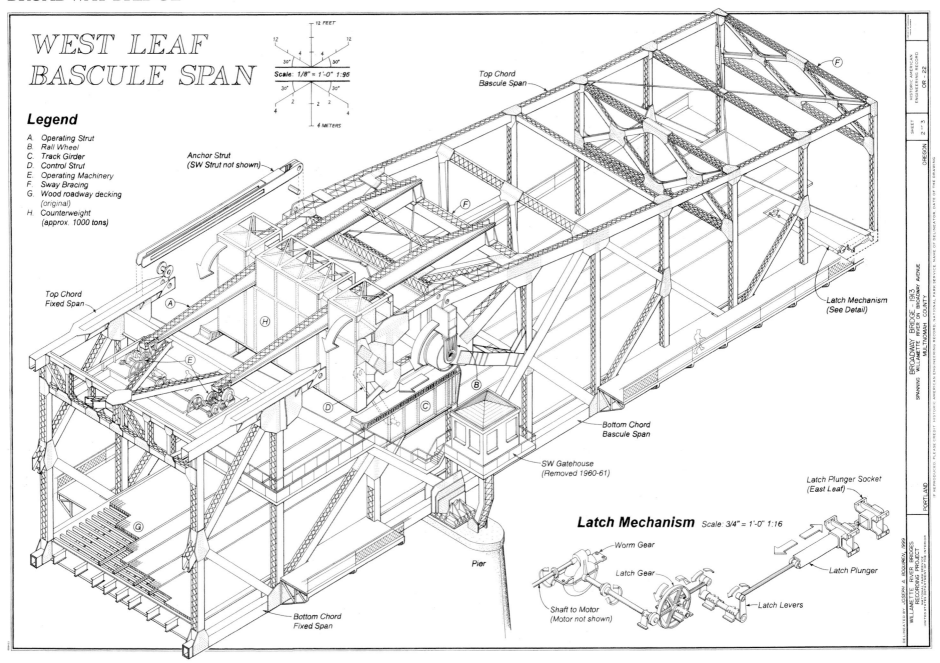

WEST LEAF BASCULE SPAN

Scale: 1/8" = 1'-0" 1:96

12 FEET

4 METERS

Legend

A. Operating Strut
B. Rail Wheel
C. Track Girder
D. Control Strut
E. Operating Machinery
F. Sway Bracing
G. Wood roadway decking
    (original)
H. Counterweight
    (approx. 1000 tons)

Anchor Strut
(SW Strut not shown)

Top Chord
Bascule Span

Top Chord
Fixed Span

Latch Mechanism
(See Detail)

Bottom Chord
Bascule Span

SW Gatehouse
(Removed 1960-61)

Pier

Bottom Chord
Fixed Span

Latch Mechanism Scale: 3/4" = 1'-0" 1:16

Latch Plunger Socket
(East Leaf)

Worm Gear

Latch Gear

Latch Plunger

Shaft to Motor
(Motor not shown)

Latch Levers

BROADWAY BRIDGE - 1913
SPANNING WILLAMETTE RIVER ON BROADWAY AVENUE
MULTNOMAH COUNTY
PORTLAND
OREGON

HISTORIC AMERICAN
ENGINEERING RECORD
OR - 22

SHEET 2 OF 3

WILLAMETTE RIVER BRIDGES
RECORDING PROJECT
DELINEATED BY JOSEPH A. BOGREN, 1999

144

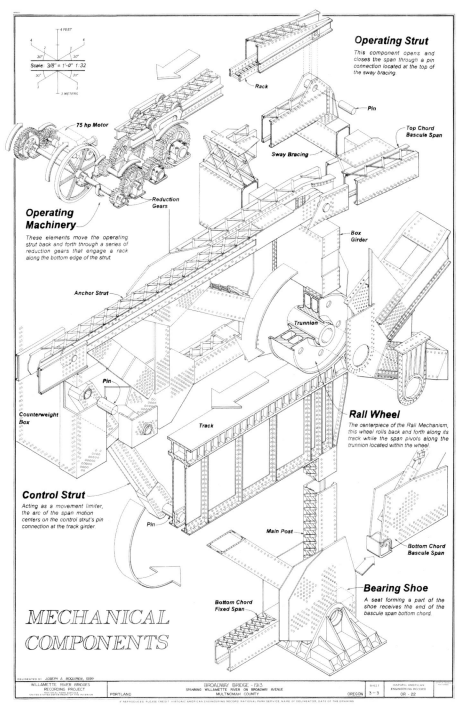

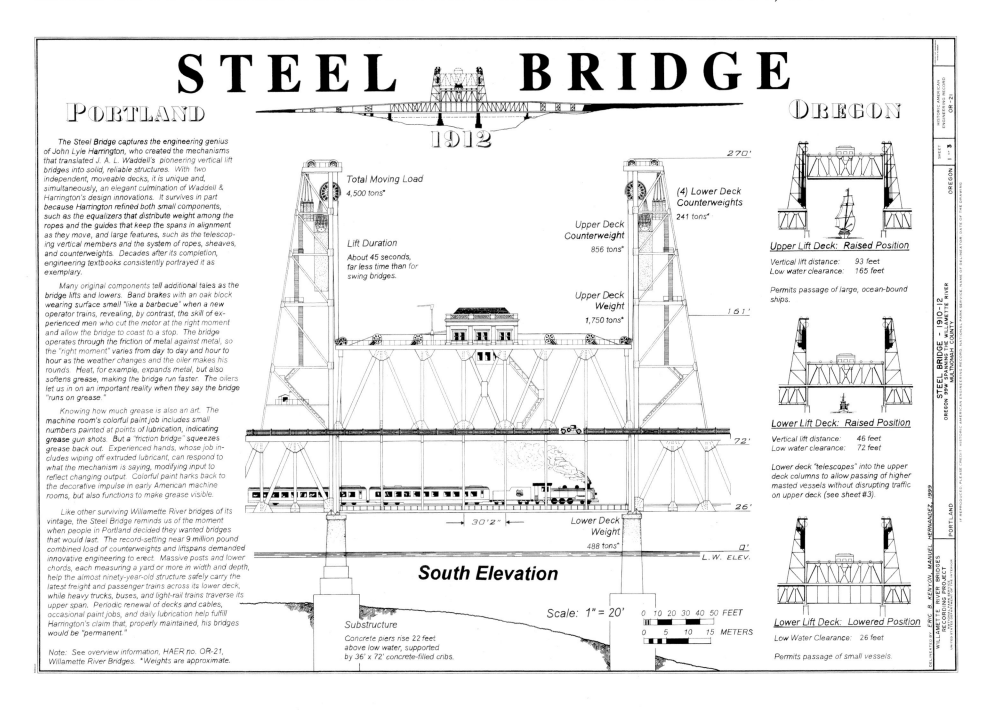

STEEL BRIDGE

PORTLAND

OREGON

1912

The *Steel Bridge* captures the engineering genius of John Lyle Harrington, who created the mechanisms that translated J. A. L. Waddell's pioneering vertical lift bridges into solid, reliable structures. With two independent, moveable decks, it is unique and, simultaneously, an elegant culmination of Waddell & Harrington's design innovations. It survives in part because Harrington refined both small components, such as the equalizers that distribute weight among the ropes and the guides that keep the spans in alignment as they move, and large features, such as the telescoping vertical members and the system of ropes, sheaves, and counterweights. Decades after its completion, engineering textbooks consistently portrayed it as exemplary.

Many original components tell additional tales as the bridge lifts and lowers. Band brakes with an oak block wearing surface smell "like a barbecue" when a new operator trains, revealing, by contrast, the skill of experienced men who cut the motor at the right moment and allow the bridge to coast to a stop. The bridge operates through the friction of metal against metal, so the "right moment" varies from day to day and hour to hour as the weather changes and the oiler makes his rounds. Heat, for example, expands metal, but also softens grease, making the bridge run faster. The oilers let us in on an important reality when they say the bridge "runs on grease."

Knowing how much grease is also an art. The machine room's colorful paint job includes small numbers painted at points of lubrication, indicating grease gun shots. But a "friction bridge" squeezes grease back out. Experienced hands, whose job includes wiping off extruded lubricant, can respond to what the mechanism is saying, modifying input to reflect changing output. Colorful paint harks back to the decorative impulse in early American machine rooms, but also functions to make grease visible.

Like other surviving Willamette River bridges of its vintage, the Steel Bridge reminds us of the moment when people in Portland decided they wanted bridges that would last. The record-setting near 9 million pound combined load of counterweights and liftspans demanded innovative engineering to erect. Massive posts and lower chords, each measuring a yard or more in width and depth, help the almost ninety-year-old structure safely carry the latest freight and passenger trains across its lower deck, while heavy trucks, buses, and light-rail trains traverse its upper span. Periodic renewal of decks and cables, occasional paint jobs, and daily lubrication help fulfill Harrington's claim that, properly maintained, his bridges would be "permanent."

Note: See overview information, HAER no. OR-21, Willamette River Bridges. *Weights are approximate.

Total Moving Load
4,500 tons*

Lift Duration
About 45 seconds, far less time than for swing bridges.

Upper Deck Counterweight
856 tons*

Upper Deck Weight
1,750 tons*

(4) Lower Deck Counterweights
241 tons*

270'

161'

72'

26'

0'
L.W. ELEV.

← 30'2" →

Lower Deck Weight
488 tons*

South Elevation

Substructure
Concrete piers rise 22 feet above low water, supported by 36' x 72' concrete-filled cribs.

Scale: 1" = 20'

0 10 20 30 40 50 FEET

0 5 10 15 METERS

Upper Lift Deck: Raised Position

Vertical lift distance: 93 feet
Low water clearance: 165 feet

Permits passage of large, ocean-bound ships.

Lower Lift Deck: Raised Position

Vertical lift distance: 46 feet
Low water clearance: 72 feet

Lower deck "telescopes" into the upper deck columns to allow passing of higher masted vessels without disrupting traffic on upper deck (see sheet #3).

Lower Lift Deck: Lowered Position

Low Water Clearance: 26 feet

Permits passage of small vessels.

DELINEATED BY: ERIC B. KENYON, MANUEL HERNANDEZ, 1999

WILLAMETTE RIVER BRIDGES RECORDING PROJECT

PORTLAND

STEEL BRIDGE - 1910-12
OREGON 99W SPANNING THE WILLAMETTE RIVER
MULTNOMAH COUNTY

OREGON

HISTORIC AMERICAN ENGINEERING RECORD
OR-21

SHEET 1 OF 3

STEEL BRIDGE

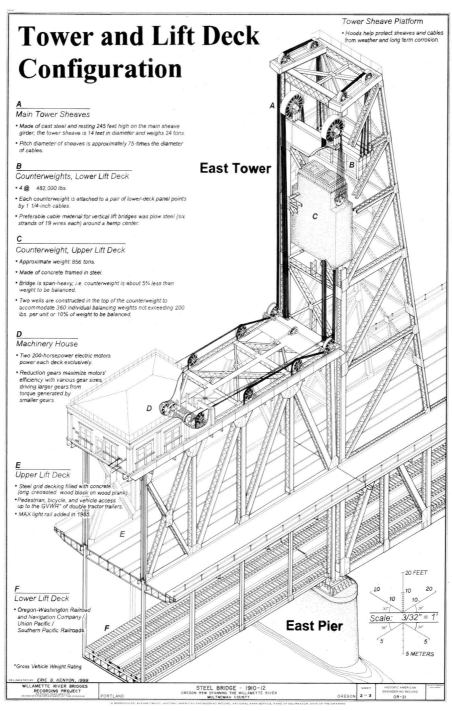

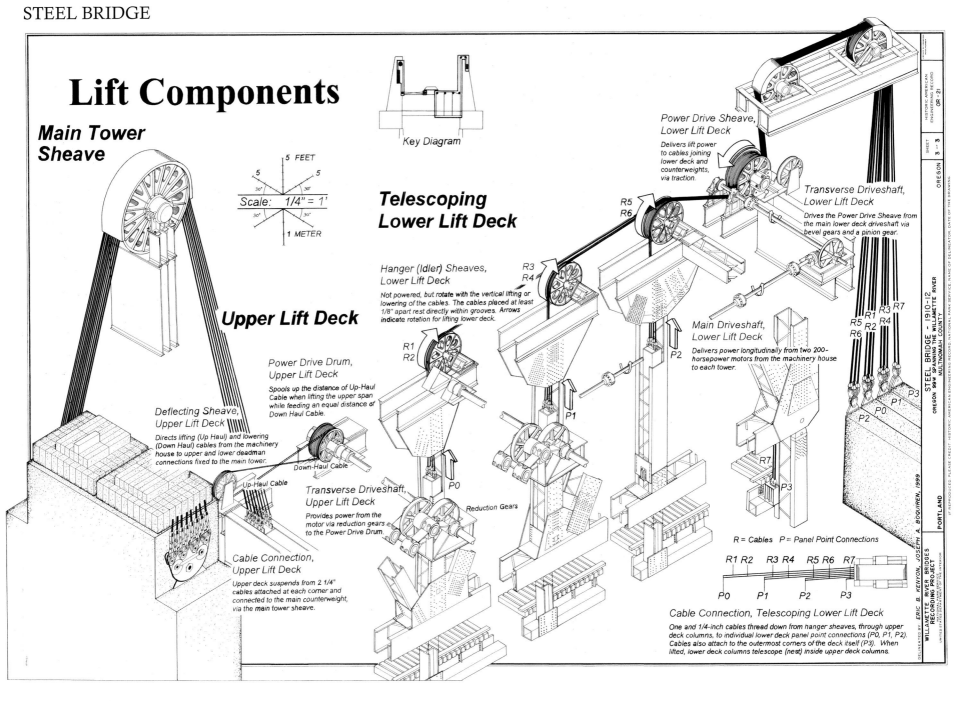

Lift Components

Main Tower Sheave

Key Diagram

5 FEET

Scale: 1/4" = 1'

1 METER

Telescoping Lower Lift Deck

Upper Lift Deck

Power Drive Sheave, Lower Lift Deck
Delivers lift power to cables joining lower deck and counterweights, via traction.

Transverse Driveshaft, Lower Lift Deck
Drives the Power Drive Sheave from the main lower deck driveshaft via bevel gears and a pinion gear.

Hanger (Idler) Sheaves, Lower Lift Deck
Not powered, but rotate with the vertical lifting or lowering of the cables. The cables placed at least 1/8" apart rest directly within grooves. Arrows indicate rotation for lifting lower deck.

R5
R6

R3
R4

R1
R2

P1

P2

Main Driveshaft, Lower Lift Deck
Delivers power longitudinally from two 200-horsepower motors from the machinery house to each tower.

R1 R3 R7
R5 R2 R4
R6

P3

P0
P1

P2

Power Drive Drum, Upper Lift Deck
Spools up the distance of Up-Haul Cable when lifting the upper span while feeding an equal distance of Down Haul Cable.

Deflecting Sheave, Upper Lift Deck
Directs lifting (Up Haul) and lowering (Down Haul) cables from the machinery house to upper and lower deadman connections fixed to the main tower.

Down-Haul Cable

Up-Haul Cable

P1

P0

R7

P3

Transverse Driveshaft, Upper Lift Deck
Provides power from the motor via reduction gears to the Power Drive Drum.

Reduction Gears

Cable Connection, Upper Lift Deck
Upper deck suspends from 2 1/4" cables attached at each corner and connected to the main counterweight, via the main tower sheave.

R = Cables   P = Panel Point Connections

R1 R2   R3 R4   R5 R6   R7

P0   P1   P2   P3

Cable Connection, Telescoping Lower Lift Deck
One and 1/4-inch cables thread down from hanger sheaves, through upper deck columns, to individual lower deck panel point connections (P0, P1, P2). Cables also attach to the outermost corners of the deck itself (P3). When lifted, lower deck columns telescope (nest) inside upper deck columns.

HISTORIC AMERICAN ENGINEERING RECORD
OREGON   OR-21   SHEET 3 "" 3

STEEL BRIDGE — 1910-12
OREGON 99W SPANNING THE WILLAMETTE RIVER
MULTNOMAH COUNTY

PORTLAND

WILLAMETTE RIVER BRIDGES RECORDING PROJECT

DELINEATED BY ERIC B. KENYON, JOSEPH A. BOQUIREN, 1999

MOVABLE BRIDGE DRAWINGS, BY JOSEPH BOQUIREN

BROADWAY BRIDGE: RALL ROLLING-LIFT BASCULE

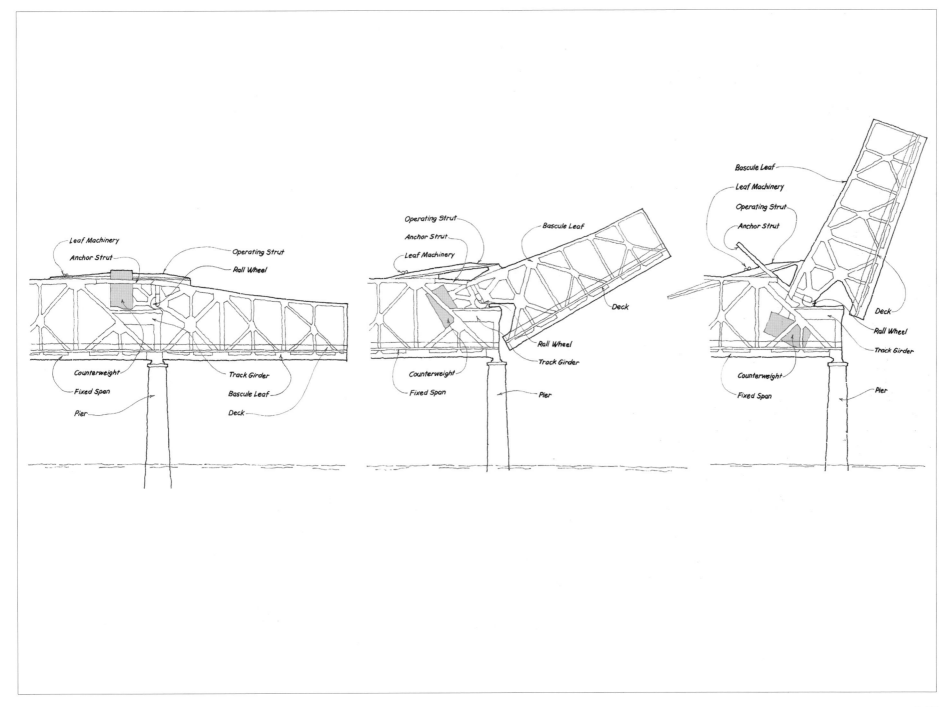

MOVABLE BRIDGE DRAWINGS
BURNSIDE BRIDGE: STRAUSS TRUNNION BASCULE

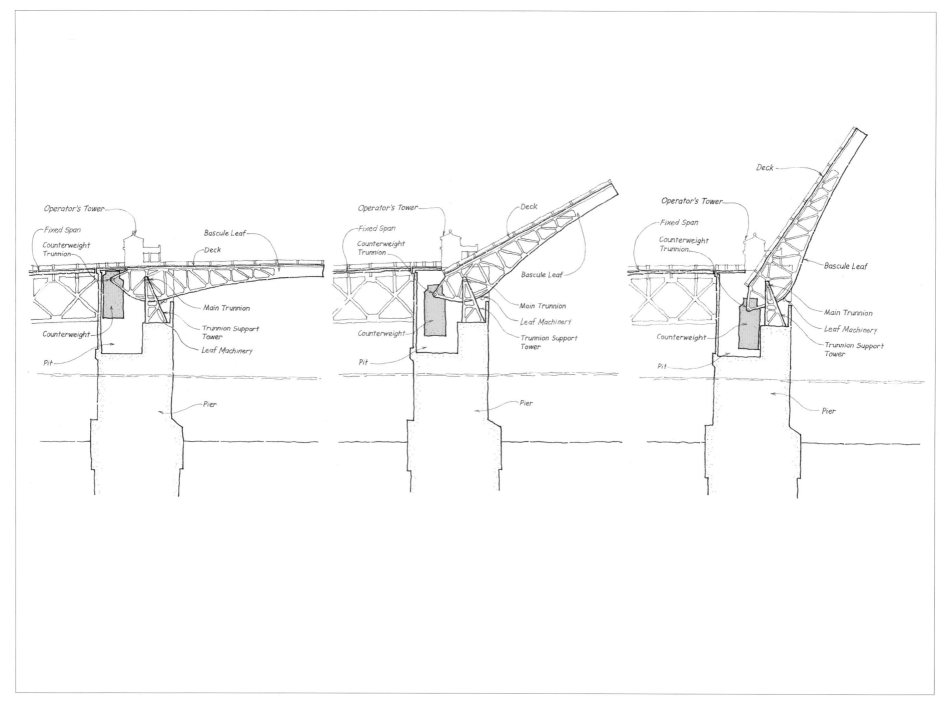

MOVABLE BRIDGE DRAWINGS

MORRISON BRIDGE: CHICAGO-STYLE (FIXED TRUNNION) BASCULE

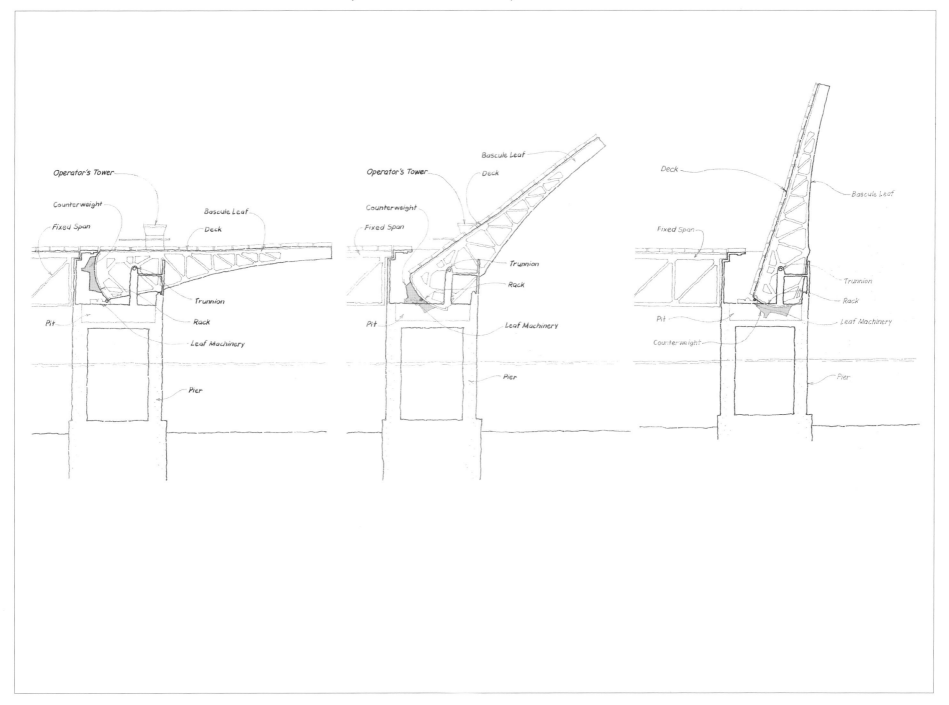

MOVABLE BRIDGE DRAWINGS
HAWTHORNE BRIDGE: VERTICAL LIFT

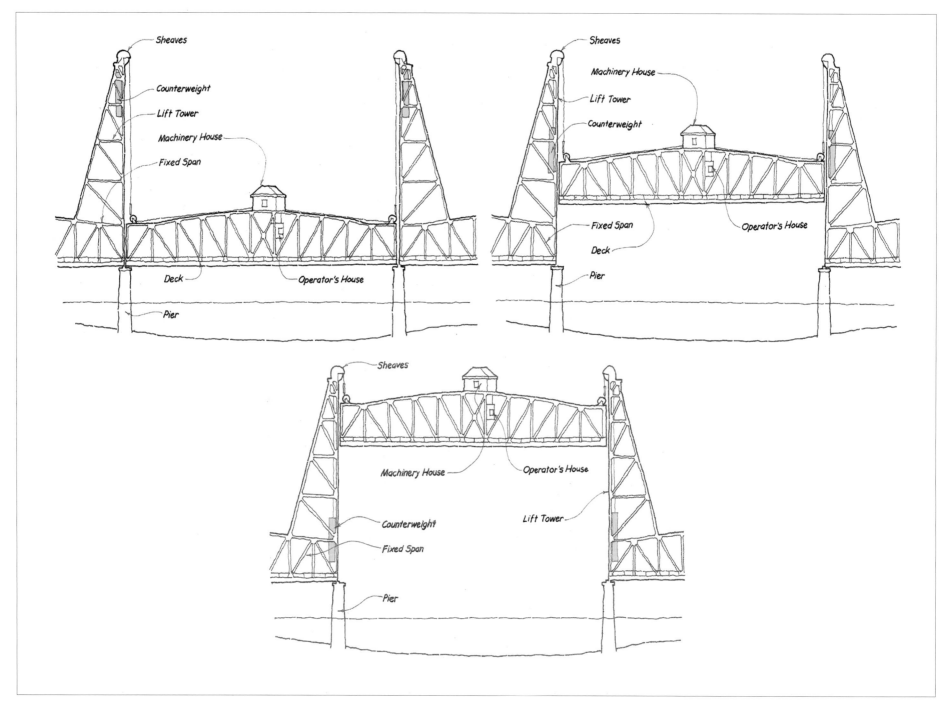

MOVABLE BRIDGE DRAWINGS

STEEL BRIDGE: DOUBLE-DECK VERTICAL LIFT WITH DUAL LIFT SYSTEMS

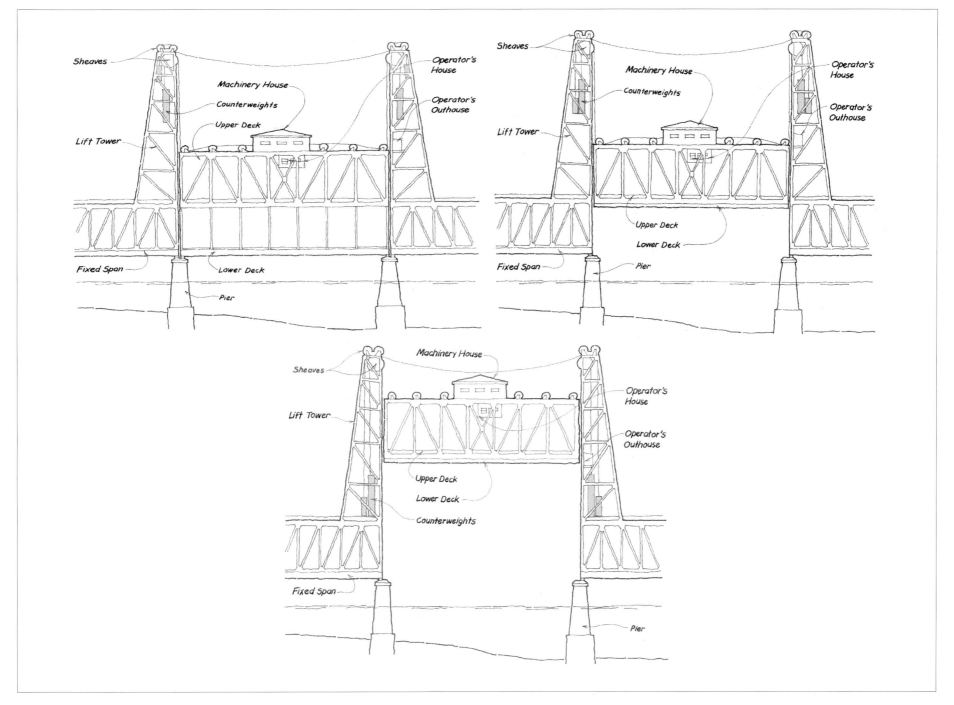

MOVABLE BRIDGE DRAWINGS

SWING BRIDGE: EXAMPLE SHOWN IS ORIGINAL (1908) RAILROAD BRIDGE 5.1

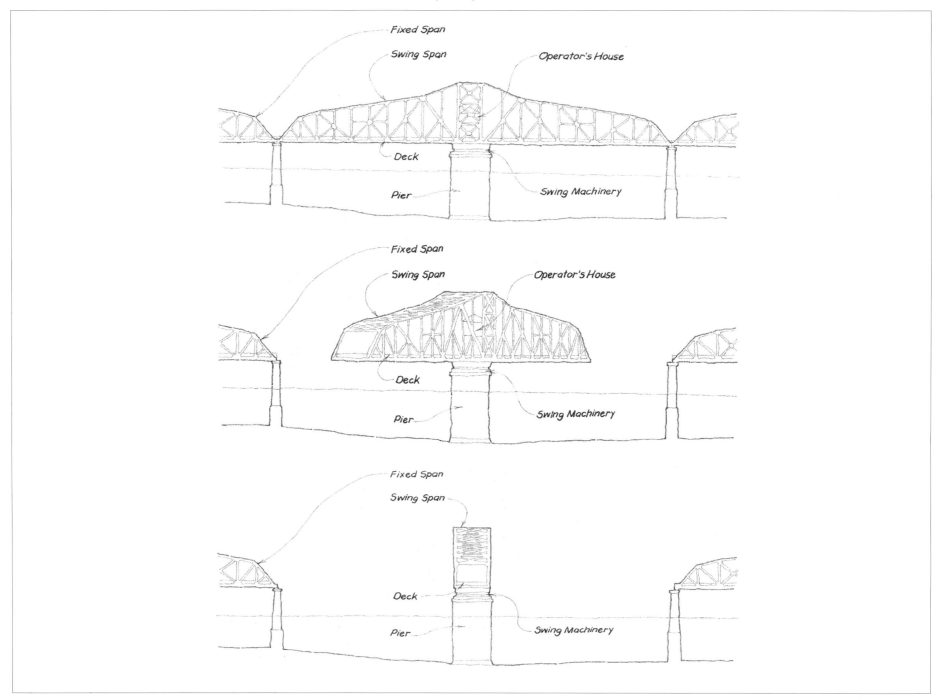

JACKING SYSTEM FOR FREMONT BRIDGE
6,000-TON CENTER SPAN LIFT, 1973

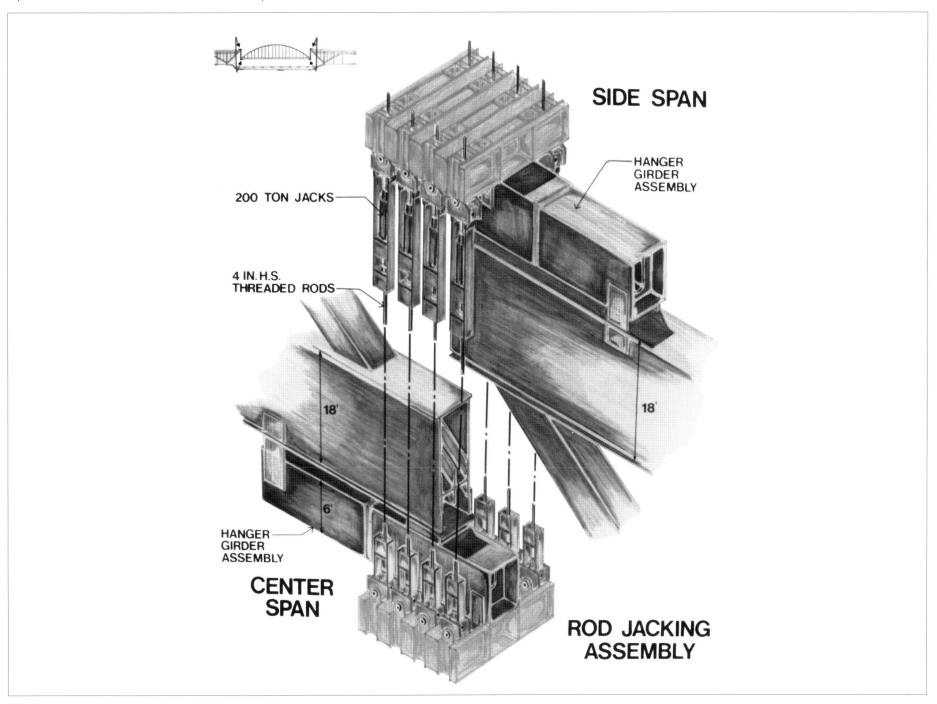

SIDE SPAN

HANGER GIRDER ASSEMBLY

200 TON JACKS

4 IN. H.S. THREADED RODS

18'

18'

6'

HANGER GIRDER ASSEMBLY

CENTER SPAN

ROD JACKING ASSEMBLY

155

COMMON HISTORIC TRUSS DESIGNS

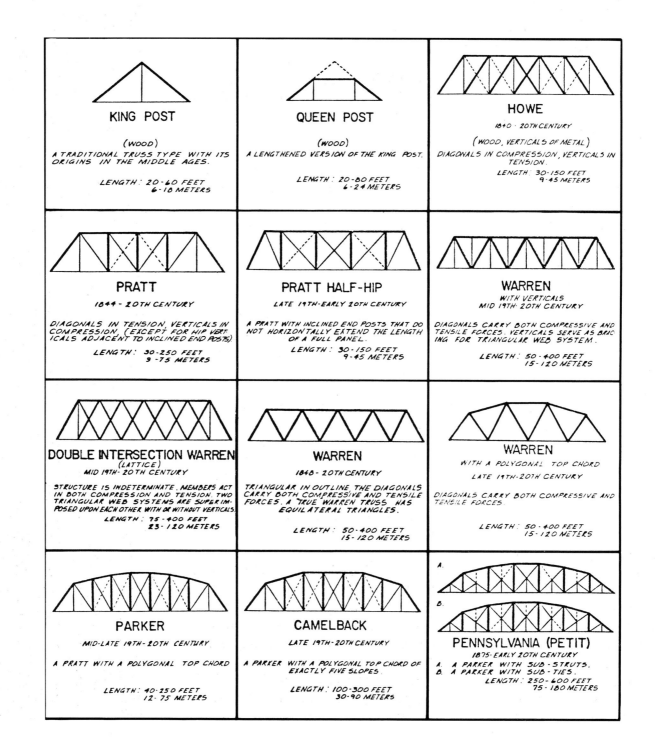

KING POST

(WOOD)

A TRADITIONAL TRUSS TYPE WITH ITS ORIGINS IN THE MIDDLE AGES.

LENGTH: 20-60 FEET
6-18 METERS

QUEEN POST

(WOOD)

A LENGTHENED VERSION OF THE KING POST.

LENGTH: 20-80 FEET
6-24 METERS

HOWE

1840 - 20TH CENTURY

(WOOD, VERTICALS OF METAL)

DIAGONALS IN COMPRESSION, VERTICALS IN TENSION.

LENGTH: 30-150 FEET
9-45 METERS

PRATT

1844 - 20TH CENTURY

DIAGONALS IN TENSION, VERTICALS IN COMPRESSION. (EXCEPT FOR HIP VERTICALS ADJACENT TO INCLINED END POSTS)

LENGTH: 30-250 FEET
9-75 METERS

PRATT HALF-HIP

LATE 19TH-EARLY 20TH CENTURY

A PRATT WITH INCLINED END POSTS THAT DO NOT HORIZONTALLY EXTEND THE LENGTH OF A FULL PANEL.

LENGTH: 30-150 FEET
9-45 METERS

WARREN

WITH VERTICALS
MID 19TH- 20TH CENTURY

DIAGONALS CARRY BOTH COMPRESSIVE AND TENSILE FORCES. VERTICALS SERVE AS BRACING FOR TRIANGULAR WEB SYSTEM.

LENGTH: 50-400 FEET
15-120 METERS

DOUBLE INTERSECTION WARREN

(LATTICE)

MID 19TH- 20TH CENTURY

STRUCTURE IS INDETERMINATE. MEMBERS ACT IN BOTH COMPRESSION AND TENSION. TWO TRIANGULAR WEB SYSTEMS ARE SUPERIMPOSED UPON EACH OTHER WITH OR WITHOUT VERTICALS.

LENGTH: 75-400 FEET
23-120 METERS

WARREN

1848 - 20TH CENTURY

TRIANGULAR IN OUTLINE, THE DIAGONALS CARRY BOTH COMPRESSIVE AND TENSILE FORCES. A TRUE WARREN TRUSS HAS EQUILATERAL TRIANGLES.

LENGTH: 50-400 FEET
15-120 METERS

WARREN

WITH A POLYGONAL TOP CHORD

LATE 19TH-20TH CENTURY

DIAGONALS CARRY BOTH COMPRESSIVE AND TENSILE FORCES.

LENGTH: 50-400 FEET
15-120 METERS

PARKER

MID-LATE 19TH-20TH CENTURY

A PRATT WITH A POLYGONAL TOP CHORD

LENGTH: 40-250 FEET
12-75 METERS

CAMELBACK

LATE 19TH-20TH CENTURY

A PARKER WITH A POLYGONAL TOP CHORD OF EXACTLY FIVE SLOPES.

LENGTH: 100-300 FEET
30-90 METERS

PENNSYLVANIA (PETIT)

1875-EARLY 20TH CENTURY

A. A PARKER WITH SUB-STRUTS.
B. A PARKER WITH SUB-TIES.

LENGTH: 250-600 FEET
75-180 METERS

BRIDGE GLOSSARY
TECHNICAL TERMS IN ORDINARY LANGUAGE

WORDS IN SMALL CAPITAL LETTERS HAVE THEIR OWN ENTRIES

Abernethy Bridge One of eight FIXED SPAN highway bridges on the last 26 miles of the Willamette River and its Multnomah Channel and sometimes referred to as the West Linn I-205 Bridge. Portland consulting engineers Moffat, Nichol & Bonney designed Abernethy for the Oregon State Highway Department, now known as the Oregon Department of Transportation (ODOT). Opened in 1970, it is a series of steel PLATE GIRDER and BOX GIRDER spans and is actually two independent structures. It carries vehicles and water across the Willamette between West Linn and Oregon City.

Abutment Support at each end of a bridge where the ROADWAY meets the ground. An abutment may include a retaining wall to hold dirt in place. Prominent abutments and retaining walls can be seen while traveling the I-405 freeway west of downtown Portland. (See SUBSTRUCTURE)

Alloy Mixture of metals. See CAST IRON, STEEL and WROUGHT IRON.

Aluminum Strong, lightweight metal used for many products from kitchen pans to ships and airplanes. Aluminum is not often used in bridges because of its high cost relative to STEEL. Occasionally, bridge ENGINEERS use aluminum in order to save weight, as for sidewalks on movable bridges. New aluminum sidewalks were installed on the Hawthorne Bridge LIFT SPAN in 1999 for this reason. Another

example is the aluminum sidewalk installed on the Steel Bridge in 2001 as part of RIVERWALK.

Anchorage CABLES are the main supports for SUSPENSION BRIDGES. An anchorage holds the cables in place, and attaches the cables to the ground. The east end anchorage of the St. Johns suspension bridge, located in Cathedral Park, is hollow and weighs 29,000 tons.

Approach Structure that carries traffic from land onto the main part of the bridge. Most of the Portland Central City waterfront bridges have long approaches on their eastern ends.

Aqueduct Conduit used for carrying water great distances over a river or valley. Aqueducts built by the Romans can still be seen in Spain and France, some of them 2,000 years old. The Ross Island and Abernethy bridges carry water in pipes across the Willamette River, the only two aqueducts across the Willamette River in Portland.

Arch bridge One of three main bridge types, the others being BEAM and SUSPENSION bridges. An arch is a curved structure that acts in COMPRESSION—forces pushing together in the arch hold the bridge up. Arch bridges can have the ROADWAY DECK located on top of the arch (Crooked River Gorge Bridge and VISTA AVENUE VIADUCT), through the arch (Oregon City and

Abernethy Bridge

Fremont bridges), or at the bottom of the arch (McLoughlin Bridge and 2008 Sauvie Island). Arch bridges date to ancient times, and may have developed from forms of stone CANTILEVERS.

Architect Someone who usually designs buildings. Architects may help shape the features of a bridge, assisting the design engineer who is responsible for the bridge's structural form. The architectural firm Houghtaling and Dougan of Portland designed details of the Burnside and Ross Island bridges. Another architectural firm, H2L2 of New York, helped develop aesthetic details for the 2008 Sauvie Island Bridge.

Balustrade Decorative railing, usually constructed of concrete or stone. The individual posts are called balusters. The balustrade on the Burnside Bridge is approximately 1,200 feet long per side.

Bascule bridge One of three main movable bridge types, the others being VERTICAL LIFT and SWING bridges. Bascule is a French word meaning seesaw. A bascule bridge allows the ROADWAY to tilt up out of the way of river traffic using COUNTERWEIGHTS to balance the weight of the LIFT SPAN. Bascule bridges are one of two types, either SINGLE-LEAF (with one hinge) or DOUBLE-LEAF (with two hinges). Broadway, Burnside, and Morrison bridges, the three bascule bridges over the Willamette River in Portland, are all double-leaf bascules. A single-leaf bascule is located across Navigation Lock No. 4 at Willamette Falls. (See Broadway, Burnside, and Morrison bridges and OVERHEAD COUNTERWEIGHT-TYPE BASCULE)

Bascule pit Space inside a bascule bridge housing the COUNTERWEIGHT. The bascule pits of the Morrison Bridge, one on each side of the center span and below the operator houses, are three stories deep. Not all bascule bridges have bascule pits. The Broadway Bridge's two counterweights are located in the open above the roadway deck.

Beam bridge One of three main bridge types, the others being ARCH and SUSPENSION bridges. A beam is a type of structure that carries loads in BENDING. Possibly the first beam bridge was a downed tree, placed across a stream or canyon so that people could walk across. Large beams spanning between main supports are called GIRDERS. A variation of a beam bridge is the TRUSS BRIDGE. (See Glenn L. Jackson and Abernethy bridges)

Bearing Two general types of bearings are used on bridges: structural and mechanical. Structural bearings transmit LOADS from a bridge to its supports (see ABUTMENT, BENT, and PIER). These bearings are designed to allow the bridge to move relative to its supports due to BENDING and temperature changes. Two prominent structural bearings, painted tan, can be seen under the east end of the Burnside Bridge, just above the public skateboard park. Also look for the four 13-foot tall green bearings supporting the Fremont Bridge, two on each side of the Willamette River. Mechanical bearings are used in the machinery to operate the lift spans on movable bridges. These bearings support the shafts or TRUNNIONS that fit through moving parts such as gears and SHEAVES.

Bending Loads on a BEAM BRIDGE produce bending. Bending is a combination of COMPRESSION FORCES in one side of the beam and TENSION FORCES in the opposite side. By definition, all beams bend; if it does not bend, it is not a beam.

Bent Upright tower on land that supports a bridge. An upright tower in water that supports a bridge is called a PIER. Bents and piers are parts of a bridge's SUBSTRUCTURE. (The words BENT and BENDING as used here are not related.) All the Central City waterfront bridges feature multiple bents supporting their APPROACHES.

Box girder STEEL or CONCRETE GIRDER with a hollow cross section. Box girders are designed to give strength without excessive weight. (See Abernethy Bridge)

Bridge The word bridge is of ancient Germanic origin. According to the U.S. Federal Highway Administration, a bridge is any span or structure across an opening 20 feet or greater. Approximately 600,000 highway bridges meet this definition in the U.S. (See PONTIST)

Bridge monkey Nickname for bridge maintenance workers.

Bridge tender/operator Person who opens, closes, and helps maintain movable bridges. In 2006, ten full-time and six on-call operators staff the four movable bridges owned by Multnomah County across the Willamette River in downtown Portland. When called to make an opening, bridge operators announce on their public address systems: "Attention, all pedestrians. Stand clear of the draw span of the Hawthorne Bridge, we're having an opening. Stand clear of the automatic gates."

Brittle Instead of bending or stretching when overloaded, brittle materials break abruptly. Examples of brittle materials are glass, CAST IRON, and CONCRETE without STEEL REINFORCING bars. Materials that do stretch or bend before breaking are called DUCTILE. Rubber, some plastics, and most STEEL are examples of ductile materials. Steel can sometimes be brittle due to imperfections or the effects of WELDING. Brittle materials pose dangers because they give little warning of overloading before breaking. (See TOUGHNESS)

Broadway Bridge One of five Portland Central City MOVABLE bridges. Broadway opened in 1913. Chicago consulting engineer RALPH MODJESKI designed Broadway for the City of Portland as a steel THROUGH TRUSS bridge with a Rall BASCULE for the City of Portland. It is now owned and maintained by Multnomah County. Broadway's lift span rolls backward at the same time it tilts up, a complicated design shared by only a few other bridges in the U.S. It was the largest DOUBLE-LEAF BASCULE bridge in the U.S. at the time it was built. (See PRATT TRUSS and PENNSYLVANIA-PETIT TRUSS)

Burnside Bridge One of five Portland Central City MOVABLE bridges. Opened in 1926 by Multnomah County, Burnside's overall DECK TRUSS design is credited to Ira Hedrick with engineer GUSTAV LINDENTHAL in charge of construction. JOSEPH STRAUSS designed Burnside's BASCULE system. The

configuration of Burnside's two FIXED SPAN trusses, described as a double-intersection WARREN deck trusses with sub-verticals, is unique in Oregon. Burnside was the first large bascule bridge in the U.S. designed with a solid concrete DECK. Burnside's center span divides the city north, south, east, and west.

Cable A rope consisting of many small wires or fibers. Three general types of cables are used on bridges: structural, electrical, and fiber-optic. Structural cables made of steel wires are strong and flexible, and are often used as tension members in bridges. See CABLE-STAYED BRIDGE, SUSPENSION BRIDGE, and SUSPENDERS. Electrical cables use copper wires to carry electricity. Electrical cables called "submarine cables" are placed underwater to send electrical power from one end of a BASCULE BRIDGE to the other. Fiber-optic cables use tiny glass fibers to carry light rays. Multnomah County's MOVABLE bridges (Broadway, Burnside, Morrison, and Hawthorne) are equipped with fiber-optic cables for monitoring or controlling the lift span machinery.

Cable-stayed bridge Variation of the conventional SUSPENSION bridge. A cable-stayed bridge's ROADWAY DECK is supported by a series of straight cables attached to TOWERS and sloping down to the deck. The first major American cable-stayed bridge was the Japonski Bridge, opened in Sitka Harbor, Alaska in 1972 (main span length 450 feet). A large cable-stayed bridge opened in 1990 in downtown Tacoma. There are no cable-stayed bridges for vehicles in the Portland

Broadway Bridge

Burnside Bridge

area. (See VETERANS HOSPITAL PEDESTRIAN SKYBRIDGE)

Caisson Type of FOUNDATION for a bridge or other structure. Caissons may be used on land or in water. In general, caissons are open-bottom boxes or cylinders that are sunk into the ground, and then filled with CONCRETE or stone to support a structure. A caisson holds back the dirt and rock around the sides of the hole until it is filled. Different types of caissons are used, and vary from cylinders a few feet in diameter up to boxes 100 feet or more in width. Caissons can be made of CONCRETE, STEEL, or WOOD. Caissons are installed by digging out the dirt and rock from inside, then pushing the caisson into the ground by adding weight to it. The main river PIERS of the Burnside and Hawthorne bridges were built using the open caisson method. Timber CRIBS with open tops and bottoms were floated into place and sunk at the pier locations. Loose dirt was then dug out from inside using cranes working from the surface. For these two bridges, timber PILES were driven into the ground inside the caissons before they were filled with concrete. The four piers supporting the Broadway Bridge's river SPANS are founded on concrete-filled wooden caissons of the pneumatic (compressed air) type. Pneumatic caissons were used for construction of bridges and other facilities in the late 19th and early 20th centuries. They were made airtight so that compressed air could be pumped in to keep water and mud from flowing in under the bottom of the caisson as crews dug out dirt while working in high-pressure air. The high pressure made them vulnerable

to nitrogen poisoning, called the bends or caisson sickness. (See CRIBS, COFFERDAMS, and DRILLED SHAFTS)

Camber Upward curve built into a bridge to anticipate the DEFLECTION that will occur when LOADS are applied to the structure. Bridge walkers can easily see the camber on the VETERANS HOSPITAL PEDESTRIAN SKYBRIDGE and on the UNION STATION PEDESTRIAN BRIDGE while standing in the elevator entrances at bridge level.

Cantilever bridge Type of BEAM bridge that came into general use for long spans during the railway era, when engineers found that bridges more rigid than SUSPENSION bridges (as then built) were needed to carry heavy trains and freight. A cantilever is a bracket or arm that juts out. A cantilever bridge is made up of two such brackets or arms. A diving board is a good example of a cantilevered structural member that is anchored at one end and free-hanging at the other. Many bridges are built using the cantilever principle in order to save materials and simplify construction. In cantilever bridges, the weight of the cantilevered sections is balanced by anchor SPANS on the backside of the PIERS. Cantilever bridges typically have two cantilever sections reaching out from each end, plus a suspended section joining the two cantilever sections in mid-span. Marquam Bridge is a good example of a cantilever bridge with a suspended section in the middle. The Ross Island Bridge is an unusual example of a cantilever bridge with no suspended section. (The ends of the cantilevers in Ross Island meet in the

160

center of the bridge.) The design ENGINEER did this so that the bridge would give the greatest clearance for river traffic using the least amount of steel, thus saving money. In addition to Marquam and Ross Island, there are five other known major cantilever highway bridges in Oregon: the Astoria-Megler Bridge, Bridge of the Gods, Coos Bay Bridge, and one bridge each across the Columbia River at Rainier and at Umatilla. Although not usually recognized as such, double-leaf BASCULE bridges are a form of cantilever bridge. In bascules, the weight of the cantilevered sections is balanced by COUNTERWEIGHTS.

Casing A large steel pipe used in building DRILLED SHAFTS. The casing is first pushed or driven into the ground until it reaches solid rock or hard dirt. Loose dirt and rock are then dug out from inside the casing and the casing is filled with CONCRETE. Casings may be temporary or permanent. Temporary casings are pulled out of the ground as the concrete is placed, then used again for building other drilled shafts. Permanent casings are left in place to add strength to the drilled shafts. (See Sauvie Island Bridge)

Cast iron ALLOY of IRON and carbon containing about two percent carbon. In the 1700s and 1800s, cast iron was used to create many forms and shapes, including MEMBERS for bridge construction. However, it was not used for long in bridge construction as it is too BRITTLE to withstand large TENSILE (pulling) forces. WROUGHT IRON and STEEL also are alloys of iron and carbon. They are not as brittle as cast iron because they have less carbon.

Catenary Natural curve formed by a rope or CABLE draped under its own weight alone. When the main cables of a SUSPENSION bridge are originally installed, they hang from the bridge towers in a catenary shape. Once the DECK is hung from the cable, the shape changes from a catenary to a PARABOLIC-shaped curve. (See St. Johns Bridge)

Cathodic protection Innovative method to prevent damage to reinforced CONCRETE structures from ocean air and salt water penetrating the concrete and RUSTING the REINFORCING STEEL by forcing corrosion of a sacrificial metal instead. This is accomplished by connecting the higher energy, more active metal, called the anode, to the lower energy, less active steel, called the cathode. The connection can be made directly, as done by hot-dip GALVANIZING of highway guardrails, or by connection of ZINC blocks to steel hulls of fishing boats. The connection can also be made by supplying electrical current. The latter technique is being used by ODOT in its Historic Bridge Preservation program, which, so far, has saved five large highway bridges. Others are scheduled to be protected. The process places an arc-sprayed layer of solid zinc on the exterior of the bridge's concrete piers and railings. The zinc coating exactly follows the rich artistic detailing of the bridge. The zinc layer is then connected to the reinforcing steel through a number of heavy-duty power supplies that automatically adjust the current to ensure the exterior zinc corrodes and not the reinforcing steel. The power supplies take electrons away from the steel cathode, lessening its ability to

corrode, and give the electrons to the zinc anode, making the zinc easier to corrode. By replacing the sacrificial zinc layer every 25 to 30 years, the bridges can indefinitely survive ocean environments. ODOT's cathodic protection program was initiated and developed as a result of the loss of the Alsea Bay Bridge at Waldport, Oregon, opened in the late 1920s and replaced in 1991. (See SPALL)

Cement When cement is mixed with water, sand, and gravel, the result is CONCRETE. Cement is made out of burned lime and clay that has been mixed at the right temperature and ground into a fine powder. The powder mixed with water becomes a paste that dries rock hard.

Chord Main top or bottom structural member of a TRUSS extending from end to end. Truss chords carry the TENSILE and COMPRESSIVE forces produced by BENDING in the truss. (Bending is caused by applying LOADS on the truss.)

Cofferdam Temporary watertight enclosure built into a riverbed to permit construction of dams, bridge FOUNDATIONS or other structures "in the dry." A cofferdam normally is built in place by driving a series of interconnected PILING in a rectangular or circular pattern. The water inside the cofferdam is then pumped out, so that construction of the structure can proceed in open air. Cofferdams normally are removed when the structure is finished. Cofferdams are similar to CAISSONS. The primary difference is that cofferdams are temporary whereas caissons become a permanent part of the structure.

Clear span Horizontal distance between two adjoining supports.

Compression/Compressive force Force that tends to make something shorter, or pushes or squeezes it together. While a compressive force can shorten or push together, a TENSION OR TENSILE force makes things longer or pulls them apart. ARCH bridges are in compression, as are portions of BEAM and TRUSS bridges. CONCRETE, STEEL, and WOOD all work well in compression as long as the members are not too slender. Compression members too slender can buckle and collapse. To demonstrate buckling under compression, push on the ends of a thin piece of plastic or wood.

Concrete Concrete is used to make bridges, dams, buildings, and other types of structures. Mixing CEMENT, water, sand, and stones or crushed rock makes concrete, which dries rock-hard.

Continuous-span bridge Bridge that extends as one piece over multiple supports (PIERS and/or BENTS) without gaps or hinges, thus the STRESSES of the bridge are distributed over the entire structure. Continuous-span bridges can be built with GIRDERS or TRUSSES, and use less material than a structure made up of a series of independent SIMPLE SPANS. The Sellwood Bridge, for example, is a four-span continuous truss—a long bridge in which the entire structure is supported by five piers. One comparison would be a log supported by stones at intervals across a waterway. Constructed with two lanes of traffic 24 feet wide, but more than 1,092 feet in length over

piers extending 75 feet high above water, the Sellwood Bridge is one long, skinny, elevated "log" supported on piers above the Willamette River.

Contractor Company hired or contracted to build a bridge or other facility. The company hired by the owner to take charge of building the overall project is called the prime contractor or general contractor. The prime or general contractor often hires subcontractors to do specialized parts of the work such as foundation construction, steel erection, and installation of electrical equipment. Abhe & Svoboda of Minnesota was the prime contractor for Hawthorne Bridge's 1999 rehabilitation.

Counterweights VERTICAL LIFT and BASCULE bridges require counterweights to balance the weight of their movable SPANS. Counterweights usually are made of CONCRETE. The counterweights on Morrison and Burnside bridges are located inside the river PIERS and are out of sight. The counterweights on Hawthorne, Steel, Broadway, and Interstate bridges are located above the roadway and can be seen moving during openings. The two counterweights on the Morrison Bridge each weigh 950 tons, about half the weight of the counterweights inside the Burnside Bridge.

Covered bridge BEAM or TRUSS bridge with the roadway protected by a roof and side walls. Most covered bridges are made of wood. Covering the bridge protects the roadway from rain and snow so the bridge will last longer. In 2006, Oregon had about 50 covered bridges (defined as a bridge built to

carry vehicles), the sixth largest collection of covered bridges in the U.S., and the largest collection west of the Mississippi River.

Crib Wooden box built to sit on the bottom of a waterway and hold gravel, rock, or CONCRETE that will serve as the FOUNDATION for a bridge or other structure. If the crib is sunk into the ground, then it is called a CAISSON. Foundations for the Burnside and Hawthorne bridges include concrete-filled caissons made of timber cribs. PORTLAND'S HARBOR WALL along the west side waterfront sits on 51 timber cribs filled with gravel and rock. In Portland, timber cribs generally have been built from 12"x12" Douglas fir timbers.

Cross bracing Structural members providing lateral (sideways) support for main members.

Crown Highest point at the top of an ARCH. (See Fremont and Oregon City bridges)

Dead load Weight of the bridge itself, without traffic, or people, or birds, or snow, or wind, or rain.

Deck Surface part of a bridge that carries the ROADWAY and sidewalks on which vehicles, pedestrians, bicyclists, or trains travel. Most bridge decks built in recent years are made of CONCRETE. Decks can also be made of WOOD, STEEL, ALUMINUM, or composites such as FIBER REINFORCED POLYMER (See Broadway Bridge). Bridge decks are typically supported by systems of STRINGERS and FLOORBEAMS.

Deck truss TRUSS BRIDGE with the traffic roadway located on top of its structure.

When the roadway is between the trusses, it is called a THROUGH TRUSS bridge. Deck truss bridges on the lower Willamette River are Sellwood, Ross Island, Morrison, and Burnside bridges. Marquam Bridge, with two traffic decks, is a combination deck truss and through truss. (See HANGING DECK TRUSS)

Deflection Change in shape of a structure or MEMBER due to bending, stretching, or shrinking under LOAD. For example, a BEAM or TRUSS deflects downward when heavy loads are added. (See FLEXIBILITY and STIFFNESS)

Diagonals Sloping members of a TRUSS bridge that connect between the top CHORD and the bottom chord. The diagonals carry either TENSION or COMPRESSION, but not both at the same time. They work with the POSTS and chords to carry the LOADS to the PIERS.

Double-leaf bascule span BASCULE bridge with two leaves in its LIFT SPAN that open in the center and tilt up to make way for river traffic. Examples of double-leaf bascule bridges in Portland are Broadway, Burnside, and Morrison bridges. (See SINGLE-LEAF BASCULE)

Drawbridge Another word for a MOVABLE bridge. Bridges that crossed moats and allowed entry into castles were among the earliest drawbridges. They often were hinged at one end to aid raising and lowering. These were the first BASCULE bridges.

Drilled shaft A type of CAISSON used for FOUNDATIONS under bridges, buildings, and other structures. Drilled shafts are usually built as follows: (1) a steel pipe called a CASING is pushed or driven into the ground, (2) loose dirt and rock are dug out from inside the casing, (3) a cage made of REINFORCING STEEL (REBAR) is lowered into the empty casing, (4) the casing is filled with CONCRETE. In recent years, drilled shafts have become more common for bridge foundations due to their high strength for resisting SEISMIC FORCES as well as GRAVITY loads. Another reason for the recent popularity of drilled shafts is the ease of construction using specialized equipment that is now available. (See Sauvie Island Bridge)

Ductile Materials that stretch or BEND before they break. Examples are rubber, some plastics, and most steel. Ductile materials are the opposite of BRITTLE materials, which break abruptly. (See TOUGHNESS)

Elastic Elastic material changes shape and size when a FORCE is applied, but returns to its original shape and size when the force is removed. Materials used in bridges, such as STEEL, CONCRETE, and WOOD, remain elastic when the STRESSES applied are within normal range. Some materials, including steel, become PLASTIC when stresses exceed a certain level called the yield point or elastic limit. This means the material does not return to its original shape and size and is permanently deformed.

Engineer There are four basic categories of engineers: civil, electrical, mechanical, and chemical. Within these categories there are many specialties. For example, the field of civil engineering includes structural and GEOTECHNICAL engineers. Structural engineers calculate the LOADS that a bridge must carry and work out the arrangement and size of the bridge MEMBERS to carry the loads safely. Geotechnical engineers investigate ground conditions and advise about suitable FOUNDATIONS. MOVABLE BRIDGES require the expertise of mechanical and electrical engineers to design the machinery and electrical systems that operate the movable spans. Engineers who design highway bridges must be licensed professional engineers, since they are responsible for making bridges safe for public use. Any kind of building or facility used by the public must be designed by a licensed engineer or licensed ARCHITECT. The structural calculations for highway bridges, however, are the exclusive responsibility of licensed civil or structural engineers. The first academically trained professional engineer of the modern world was Jean Perronet (1708-1794), a French civil engineer known for the Pont de la Concorde stone arch bridge in Paris. Three of the first professional U.S. bridge engineers were Stephen Long (1784-1864), born in New Hampshire; Charles Ellet, Jr., (1810-1862), born in Pennsylvania; and John Augustus Roebling (1806-1869), born in Germany. The American Society of Civil Engineers was founded in 1852, one year after Portland was incorporated.

Excite the molecules Term used to describe what happens when a bridge moves for any reason, whether from children jumping on it, or from the wind, automobiles, or other FORCES. (See UNION STATION PEDESTRIAN BRIDGE and GALLOPING GERTIE)

Expansion joint Meeting point designed to allow movement of bridge parts due to heat and cold. Worn-out expansion joints were one of the reasons for closing roadway lanes and sidewalks on the Ross Island Bridge as part of a $12.5 million rehabilitation project in 2000-2001.

Falsework Temporary structure used as support during construction.

Fatigue The gradual weakening of a material when a FORCE is repeatedly applied and removed. A bridge must be able to withstand forces for many years without BENDING too much or breaking. To demonstrate fatigue, straighten a paper clip and bend it back and forth until it breaks.

Fiber Reinforced Polymer (FRP) Plastic strengthened with small fibers of glass, carbon or other strong materials. The fiberglass used for fishing rods and boats is one common type of FRP. ENGINEERS are now experimenting with use of FRP on bridges to take advantage of its high strength, TOUGHNESS, and light weight. Multnomah County installed a new FRP roadway deck on the Broadway Bridge's BASCULE span in 2004. This is one of the largest uses of FRP on a bridge in the United States to date. (See Broadway Bridge)

Fill Material (dirt, stone, boulders, concrete, sawdust) used to raise the ground level or to fill in space around structures. A million cubic yards of dredged material was used as fill behind the mile-long PORTLAND HARBOR WALL along the downtown waterfront. About 4,000 truckloads (40,000 cubic yards) of crushed rock fill were used to build the approach embankment (island

side) for the 2008 Sauvie Island Bridge. (See GEOTECHNICAL ENGINEERING)

Fixed arch Arch with no hinges. A fixed arch is more rigid than a hinged arch. (See VISTA AVENUE VIADUCT)

Fixed span A bridge span that is not designed to open for boats or other water traffic. A fixed span bridge is a bridge without a movable span.

Flexibility A measure of how much a structure flexes or deflects under LOAD. Similar to STIFFNESS. A "flexible" structure will flex more than a "stiff" structure under the same load. Two very flexible bridges in Portland are the VETERANS HOSPITAL PEDESTRIAN SKYBRIDGE and the UNION STATION PEDESTRIAN BRIDGE. (See DEFLECTION)

Floating bridge Type of bridge that is supported by water. In one variety of floating bridge, the structure is essentially a BEAM BRIDGE in the form of a long hollow BOX GIRDER. Vehicles ride on the top surface of the floating girder. The floating girder is held in place by large anchors on the floor of the waterway. The best-known bridges of this type are in Seattle, Washington. A 1,300-foot-long floating walkway opened in 2001 as part of Portland's VERA KATZ EASTBANK ESPLANADE. Another type of floating bridge is the PONTOON BRIDGE.

Floorbeam Bridge member running crosswise between the main GIRDERS or TRUSSES. The floorbeams support the DECK system, particularly the STRINGERS.

Footing Type of FOUNDATION for a bridge or other structure. A footing sits on firm ground or rock and distributes LOAD from the structure to the ground or rock. Sometimes called "spread footing" to reflect how it distributes the load.

Force Physical influence that moves an object or tries to move it. Forces can be from the inside (internal) or from the outside (external). Force is exerted when one bridge member pulls, pushes against, compresses, or twists another member. ENGINEERS refer to external forces as LOADS. The main types of loads on bridges include GRAVITY, wind, water pressure, earthquake (SEISMIC), and temperature changes. There are three internal forces in bridges: TENSION, COMPRESSION, and SHEAR.

Foundation Base on which a bridge, building, or other structure rests. Foundations support the frame of the structure and keep it from sinking into soft ground. For examples of foundation types, see CAISSON, DRILLED SHAFT, FOOTING, and PILE. On bridges, the foundations plus PIERS and BENTS constitute the SUBSTRUCTURE.

Fremont Bridge One of eight FIXED SPAN highway bridges on the last 26 miles of the Willamette River and its Multnomah Channel. Opened in 1973, Fremont was designed for ODOT by consulting engineers Parsons, Brinckerhoff, Quade & Douglas as a double-deck bridge for vehicles only. According to the Federal Highway Administration, Fremont is one of about 130 TIED ARCH highway bridges in the U.S. in 2006 (out of almost 600,000 highway bridges). It remains the longest bridge of any type in Oregon and is the world's second longest tied arch bridge, exceeded only by the Caiyuanba Bridge in China.

Gabion From the French, meaning, literally large cage. In construction, a wire mesh box often made of GALVANIZED steel used for erosion control. Filled with stones and used to form an ABUTMENT or retaining wall, gabions hold dirt in place. With its hillsides and rain, there are many gabions in Portland.

Galloping Gertie Nickname given the Tacoma Narrows Bridge across Puget Sound that collapsed in 1940 four months after it opened. Built narrow, long, and without stiffening TRUSSES, the $7 million steel SUSPENSION bridge was susceptible to wind, which soon caused the extremely flexible SPAN to twist and buckle until it collapsed. A film of Galloping Gertie's self-destruction ranks among the most dramatic and widely known images in science and engineering. It was the last bridge designed by ENGINEER Leon Moisseiff (1872-1943). (See TORSION)

Galvanizing Named for Luigi Galvani (1737-98), an Italian who discovered that certain chemicals produce electronic action. Galvanizing means to coat metal, especially IRON or STEEL, with ZINC to protect from decay (RUST) by water or air. The new steel grating on the deck of the HAWTHORNE BRIDGE is galvanized as are most bridge guard rails, including the new metal safety guardrail tubes installed two-high along both sides of the Ross Island Bridge in 2001. (Also see CATHODIC PROTECTION)

Gate (traffic) Barriers that swing up and down or in and out to prevent vehicles from proceeding onto the LIFT SPAN of a MOVABLE bridge during an opening. Each end of the Broadway and Hawthorne lift spans is equipped with two gates. Only one set of gates is used at each end of the Morrison and Burnside bridges.

Geotechnical engineering Branch of civil engineering in which engineers investigate ground conditions and advise about suitable FOUNDATIONS. Also referred to as soils engineering, soils mechanics, earthwork engineering, and earth science. Karl Terzaghi (1883-1963) is considered the founder and guiding spirit for applying scientific methods to calculate the properties of dirt. (See SELLWOOD BRIDGE and FILL)

Gephyrophobia From the Greek, a fear of crossing bridges. A common disorder among adults and children.

Girder Large BEAM that spans between a structure's main supports. The majority of Oregon's more than 6,500 highway bridges are girder bridges. Bridge girders can be built of CONCRETE, STEEL, or WOOD. There are concrete girders inside Morrison Bridge that support the BASCULE span and COUNTERWEIGHTS. (See PLATE GIRDER BRIDGE)

Glenn L. Jackson Memorial Bridge FIXED SPAN CONCRETE BOX GIRDER BRIDGE carrying I-205 across the Columbia River at Government Island. Opened in 1982, the bridge also accommodates bicyclists and pedestrians. It was designed by engineering consultants Sverdrup & Parcel (now Jacobs-Sverdrup)

Fremont Bridge

for the State of Oregon and was one of the first big bridges of its type in the U.S.

Governor Tom McCall Waterfront Park A little more than a mile of parkland owned and managed by Portland Parks and Recreation and located between Naito Parkway and the Willamette River. McCall Park extends south from the Steel Bridge, terminating just north of the Marquam Bridge. Development of the park set the stage for transformation of the west side waterfront as part of Portland's 1972 Downtown Plan. The park was started in the 1970s, and replaced six-lane Harbor Drive and other automobile-oriented features. It now includes the Japanese American Memorial, Ankeny Street Dock, Salmon Street Springs Fountain, Portland Police Memorial and other pedestrian-oriented plazas. Tom McCall (1913-1983), Robert Straub (1920-2002), and others led a campaign to clean up the polluted Willamette River while McCall was governor from 1967 to 1975.

Gravity Attraction of MASS toward the center of the earth; the greater the mass, the larger the pull. Mass of an object times the effect of gravity produces weight (M x G = W). For example, the weight of the Fremont Bridge is 30,000 tons. Its weight is carried to ground by four prominent BEARINGS (two each on the east and west sides of the Willamette River), each bearing transmitting 7,500 tons to earth. Of all the threats to bridge life, gravity is the most powerful.

Gusset plate Metal plate used to connect multiple parts in a TRUSS BRIDGE.

Hanging deck truss Bridge that hangs from supports at the top of the truss just below the level of the roadway. Only four hanging deck truss highway bridges remain in Oregon as of 2006. All are in Portland. Three of the four are the North Fessenden Street Overcrossing, North Lombard Street Overcrossing, and North Willamette Boulevard Overcrossing, all three designed by RALPH MODJESKI and built in 1908-09 by the Spokane, Portland, and Seattle Railroad in North Portland's Peninsula district across the Portsmouth Cut, also known as the St. Johns Cut. The fourth is the Balch Gulch Bridge, which opened in 1905 to carry Thurman Street over MacLeay Park in Northwest Portland. Another hanging truss in the Portland area is the two-span pedestrian bridge across U.S. 26 near the Beaverton Transit Center, in Washington County. However, this bridge is a THROUGH TRUSS rather than a DECK TRUSS since the pedestrian walkway is between the trusses. The structure is further unusual because the bottom CHORDS of the trusses are curved.

Hawthorne Bridge One of five Portland Central City MOVABLE bridges. Opened in 1910 by the City of Portland, the Hawthorne is now owned by Multnomah County and was the first of a series of large bridges replacing earlier SWING bridges. Hawthorne is a THROUGH TRUSS VERTICAL LIFT and was designed by Waddell & Harrington. It remains the oldest operating vertical lift bridge in the U.S. (See PARKER TRUSS)

Hinged arch Arch supported by a large PIN at each end. In a three-hinged arch, a third pin is located at the CROWN of the arch. A hinged arch is more flexible than a FIXED ARCH. (See Oregon City Bridge)

Horizontal Sideways direction level or flat with the earth. (Opposite of VERTICAL, or up and down and at right angles to the earth.) For example, a tree blown flat to the ground is in a horizontal position. The closed decks of BASCULE BRIDGES like the Morrison, Burnside, and Broadway bridges are also horizontal. When such bridges open, their decks move toward a vertical position. (Most bascule bridges do not open straight up and down a full 90 degrees, or completely vertical.)

Infrastructure 20th century term referring to physical systems or parts of systems created to support a technological civilization. For instance, sewers, electrical transmission lines, the Internet, railroad tracks, freeways, and BRIDGES are parts of city infrastructure.

Interstate Bridge VERTICAL LIFT MOVABLE TRUSS bridge carrying Interstate 5 (I-5) across the Columbia River between Portland, Oregon and Vancouver, Washington. The northbound SPAN, opened in 1917, was designed by consultants Waddell & Harrington, with the southbound span, opened in 1958, designed by ODOT. Interstate's lift span creates the only traffic stop on I-5 from Mexico to Canada.

Iron One of the basic chemical elements. Its chemical symbol is Fe from *ferrum,* the Latin word for iron. It is found in meteorites. Iron RUSTS easily and can be magnetized and is strongly attracted to magnets. Iron is the most common metal in nature and, as the main ingredient in STEEL,

is especially useful in the construction of bridges. (See ALLOY, CAST IRON, and WROUGHT IRON)

Ironworker Person who builds bridges and buildings made of structural steel.

Jersey barrier Type of semi-permanent barrier often used on bridges to help direct vehicles back toward their own travel lane and prevent them from crossing the centerline or leaving the roadway. The Jersey barrier has a specially designed face with a double-slope that helps prevent vehicles from jumping over.

Lift span MOVABLE section of a VERTICAL LIFT or BASCULE bridge.

Lindenthal, Gustav (1850-1935) One of the world's most famous early 20th century bridge engineers, Lindenthal designed, among other bridges, the Hell Gate Arch and Queensboro bridges in New York City. In Portland, he designed Ross Island Bridge and the truss spans of the Sellwood Bridge. He was also involved with the Burnside and Broadway bridges and the first Lovejoy Viaduct.

Load Type of FORCE that pushes or pulls on an object from the outside. For example, walking across a simple bridge, say a plank across a stream, you might feel the plank give or bounce from your weight. This downward push is what ENGINEERS call load. Even when no one is standing on the plank (or a bridge), the plank will sag. The sag is caused by the weight of the bridge responding to GRAVITY. The permanent weight of the bridge itself is called the DEAD LOAD and is permanent. Temporary loads on a bridge, such as people, trucks or

Hawthorne Bridge

Interstate Bridge

bicycles, wind, and earthquakes are called live loads. Rainwater, snow, and ice on bridges are also considered live loads.

Lovejoy Viaduct Half-mile long CONCRETE structure over Northwest Portland railroad yard. Designed by Gustav Lindenthal, after working in Portland for Multnomah County on the new Burnside, Ross Island, and Sellwood bridges through 1926. The old viaduct was demolished in 1999 to make way for development in the Pearl District. The new Lovejoy Viaduct, hampered by design challenges, didn't open until 2002. It is a steel structure 389 feet long. One hundred percent of the old viaduct was recycled; 11,941 tons of CONCRETE, 1,357 tons of metal, and 2,600 tons of sand—nothing went to the landfill. Some of the columns of the Lovejoy Viaduct were famous for paintings by a railroad watchman named Tom Stefopoulos in the early part of the 20th century.

Main span Longest SPAN in a multi-span bridge and located between the bridge's main PIERS, or TOWERS. When comparing bridge lengths (in the *World Almanac* and bridge engineering journals, for example), the measurement usually used is the length of the main span, not the length of the entire bridge nor the APPROACHES.

Marquam Bridge One of eight FIXED SPAN highway bridges on the last 26 miles of the Willamette River and its Multnomah Channel and one of seven major CANTILEVER TRUSS bridges in Oregon. Opened in 1966, Marquam was designed by ODOT as a double-DECK steel cantilever truss to carry vehicles only as part of I-5. (See WARREN TRUSS)

Mass Collection of matter that forms a whole. The heavier an object is, the more mass it has. Weight is mass times the effect of GRAVITY (M x G = W).

McCullough, Conde B. (1887-1946) Bridge engineer famous for the REINFORCED CONCRETE ARCH bridges built along Highway 101 on the Oregon Coast during the 1930s. McCullough also designed STEEL arch bridges, including the Oregon City Bridge and the McLoughlin Bridge at the confluence of the Clackamas and Willamette rivers. For more about McCullough see *Elegant Arches, Soaring Spans: CB McCullough, Oregon's Master Bridge Builder*, by Robert Hadlow.

Member One of the parts of a structure. Member is often used to refer to the parts of a TRUSS BRIDGE, for example, its CHORDS, DIAGONALS, POSTS, FLOORBEAMS, and STRINGERS.

Modjeski, Ralph (1861-1940) Design engineer for the Broadway Bridge in Portland, as well as BNSF Railway bridges 5.1, 8.8, and 9.6, located in North Portland, and a massive railroad bridge across Crooked River Canyon in Central Oregon. Modjeski was an internationally-known bridge engineer. One of his best-known structures is the Benjamin Franklin Bridge in Philadelphia, the world's longest SUSPENSION SPAN when it opened in 1926. (See HANGING DECK TRUSS for other Modjeski bridges in Portland)

Morrison Bridge One of five Portland Central City MOVABLE bridges. Opened in 1958 by Multnomah County, Morrison is a DECK TRUSS with a DOUBLE-LEAF BASCULE LIFT SPAN.

The consulting engineers Sverdrup & Parcel of St. Louis and Moffatt, Nichol & Taylor of Portland designed the innovative open bascule piers to permit the river to flow through. Morrison is the only non-freeway bridge integrated with Portland's interstate highway system. (See PRATT TRUSS)

Movable bridges The three main movable bridge types are SWING, VERTICAL LIFT, and BASCULE. ARCH and SUSPENSION bridges are not designed to move, so movable bridges fall into the BEAM or TRUSS category. Watercraft have the right of way on all navigable waters in the U.S., because the rivers were here first as transportation routes. For this reason, bridges must be high enough to provide clearance or move out of the way of all water-borne traffic.

Multi-span bridges A single-span bridge would be impractical or too expensive for crossing wide valleys or great rivers. Multi-span bridges are carried by a series of PIERS or BENTS set in the river or valley. It is usually less expensive to construct multiple short spans and more PIERS to carry the spans across the river. Many of the lower Willamette bridges are multi-span bridges. (See VIADUCT)

Open-spandrel In an open-spandrel ARCH bridge, the ROADWAY DECK is supported by the arch on a series of independent posts. In a closed-spandrel arch bridge, a solid wall exists between the arch and roadway deck.

Oregon City Bridge One of eight FIXED SPAN highway bridges on the last 26 miles of the Willamette River and its Multnomah Channel. Opened in 1922 by Oregon City, West Linn, Clackamas County, and

ODOT, this bridge was designed by State Bridge Engineer CONDE B. MCCULLOUGH as a steel half-through ARCH encased in CONCRETE. It was listed in the National Register of Historic Places in 2006.

Orthotropic deck STEEL ROADWAY DECK designed to carry LOADS both crosswise and lengthwise. This bridge deck type was developed in Europe after World War II to reduce deck weight and save steel. The only orthotropic deck in Oregon is the top deck on the Fremont Bridge. The deck carries traffic LOADS to the FLOORBEAMS and GIRDERS, and also serves as part of the lengthwise tie system for the TIED ARCH.

Overhead counterweight-type bascule Type of BASCULE BRIDGE with the COUNTERWEIGHT located above the ROADWAY DECK. The counterweight pushes down on the MOVABLE span through vertical links, thereby balancing the bridge. The only overhead counterweight-type bascule in the Portland area is a SINGLE-LEAF pedestrian bridge located across Navigation Lock No. 4 at Willamette Falls.

Overpass or overcrossing Bridge crossing another roadway or railroad track. Many examples of overpasses or overcrossings exist along the I-5, I-84, I-205, and I-405 freeways in Portland. Sometimes referred to as "underpass" or "undercrossing."

Parabola/Parabolic Curved shape, such as the curve of the main cables of a suspension bridge. (See CATENARY)

Parker truss Type of TRUSS. The top CHORD of a Parker truss is curved upward. The DIAGONALS slope downward toward the

Marquam Bridge

Morrison Bridge

middle of the truss. All six truss SPANS on the Hawthorne Bridge are Parker trusses. The THROUGH TRUSS MAIN SPAN on the 1950 Sauvie Island Bridge is a Parker truss. (See PRATT TRUSS, PENNSYLVANIA-PETIT TRUSS, and WARREN TRUSS)

Pennsylvania-Petit truss Type of TRUSS. A Pennsylvania-Petit truss is similar to a Parker truss except that the main triangles are sub-divided into smaller triangles. In the past, Pennsylvania-Petit trusses were often used for longer SPANS than PARKER or PRATT trusses. Four of the FIXED spans on the Broadway Bridge are Pennsylvania-Petit trusses. (See WARREN TRUSS)

Pier Bridge supports located in water are called piers. Supports located on land are called BENTS. Piers and bents are upright (VERTICAL) supports or columns under the bridge. The piers and bents are parts of the bridge SUBSTRUCTURE.

Piles/Piling/Pilings Type of FOUNDATION used for bridges or other structures. Piles are long, slender columns driven into the ground to support the structure's weight. Piles are made of various materials and shapes. Modern bridges use STEEL or PRECAST CONCRETE piles. Morrison and Fremont bridges sit on steel piles. Older bridges, particularly those built before World War II, use timber piles. Burnside and Hawthorne bridges are supported by hundreds of timber piles made from Douglas fir tree trunks. Piles also are used to hold back the horizontal pressure from soil or water. Typical uses of this kind of piling include retaining walls, docks, and COFFERDAMS. The terms piles, piling, and

pilings are used interchangeably, with "pile" generally referring to individual pieces, and "piling" and "pilings" to a collection of pieces.

Pin-connected In early TRUSS BRIDGE construction, during the 19th and early 20th centuries, truss members were joined by large metal pins. One of the oldest pin-connected bridges in Oregon is the Balch Gulch Bridge on Thurman Street in Northwest Portland. Dating to 1905, it is the oldest bridge owned by the City of Portland. Later truss bridges used RIVETS or bolts instead of pins to join the MEMBERS.

Plans Set of drawings that show how to build a bridge, building, road, or other project. Plans for bridges are made by ENGINEERS. Plans for buildings usually are made by ARCHITECTS and ENGINEERS working together. Plans and SPECIFICATIONS are used to guide construction of the project. (See Sauvie Island Bridge)

Plastic Some materials, including steel, become plastic when stresses exceed a certain level called the yield point or ELASTIC limit. This means the material does not return to its original shape and size and is permanently deformed.

Plate girder bridge Plate GIRDERS are large STEEL BEAMS made of individual steel plates joined together with RIVETS, bolts, or WELDS. The first plate girder bridge in the U.S. was built in 1847 in Maryland for the Baltimore & Susquehanna Railroad. It was a single-track DECK girder structure with a clear SPAN of 54 feet. The design introduced the girder as a practical bridge type for short spans.

Pontist Eric DeLony, chief of the Historic American Engineering Record, National Park Service, 1987-2003, coined this phrase to describe someone who sees bridges as something beyond the ordinary. To a pontist, bridges are more than utilitarian structures that provide ways to get from one point to another. The word "Pont" or "Ponte"—used by Latin countries for bridge—has come down from Roman times and is related to the word "Pontiff." According to *Bridges in History and Legend*, by Wilbur J. Watson and Sara Ruth Watson, at one time, bridges in Rome were built and maintained by the Chief Priests who assumed the title of pontifices—a title that is said to be the origin of the word Pope, the Holy Pontiff. (See BRIDGE)

Pontoon bridge Variety of FLOATING BRIDGE. The bridge SPANS are supported on pontoons, which are barges anchored in position to support the structure. The structures for the spans typically are lightweight TRUSSES or GIRDERS. Pontoon bridges are often used by the military or in emergency situations since they can be installed quickly.

Portland Aerial Tram CABLE-supported transport system opening in 2007 to carry medical staff, patients, and the general public 3,300 feet between Oregon Health & Science University's new South Waterfront campus and the main campus on "Pill Hill."

Portland Harbor Wall Urban renewal project reclaiming 20 city blocks. Dedicated 7 June 1929, the one-mile-long wall extends from the Steel Bridge to the Hawthorne Bridge and was designed as a dam to keep floods off the streets and out of the basements of west side businesses. It also contained the first sewer system to catch the west side's waste. The ingeniously engineered structure is like an iceberg, with most of its mass below waterline. The 51 gigantic timber CRIBS, all filled with gravel, support the CONCRETE part of the wall and can only be glimpsed during very low water. Drawings illustrating the cribs can be seen on one of the interpretive panels along the VERA KATZ EASTBANK ESPLANADE.

Post VERTICAL MEMBER in a TRUSS BRIDGE that helps carry the LOAD to the PIERS, in combination with the DIAGONALS and CHORDS.

Pratt truss Type of TRUSS. In a Pratt truss, the top and bottom CHORDS are straight. The DIAGONALS slope downward toward the middle of the truss. All three truss SPANS on the Steel Bridge are Pratt trusses. The two FIXED truss spans on the Morrison Bridge are Pratt trusses. The Broadway Bridge has one Pratt truss SPAN at the east end of the bridge. (See PARKER TRUSS, PENNSYLVANIA-PETIT TRUSS, and WARREN TRUSS)

Precast concrete Concrete that has been cast into components before being placed in position. Precast concrete parts commonly used in bridge construction include DECK panels, GIRDERS, PIER sections, and PILES. The west approach to the Hawthorne Bridge is made up of precast concrete girders. Generally, precast girders are PRESTRESSED.

Prestressed concrete Concrete put in a state of COMPRESSION before LOADS are applied. The purpose of prestressing is to minimize TENSILE FORCES in the concrete (because concrete tends to break when pulled). Prestressing typically

Oregon City Bridge

Ross Island Bridge

is done by stretching STEEL bars or wires, then transferring the stretching forces to the concrete. In one type of prestressing, called pre-tensioning, bars or wires are stretched before the concrete is cast around them. In the other common type of prestressing, called post-tensioning, the bars or wires are stretched after the concrete has been cast.

Reinforced concrete Combination of concrete and reinforcing material. Concrete is very strong in COMPRESSION (when pushed), but not strong in TENSION (when pulled). To carry TENSILE FORCES, concrete normally is reinforced with other materials. The most common reinforcing materials are STEEL bars, called REINFORCING STEEL or REBAR. The rebar is placed inside the forms before the concrete is cast. Other types of reinforcing used include small fibers made of metal, plastic, or organic materials.

Reinforcing steel/rebar Round STEEL bars that are placed in the CONCRETE in bridges and other structures in order to improve the CONCRETE's capacity to carry TENSILE FORCES and to reduce cracking.

Riprap Large rocks placed to protect structures or embankments from moving water along stream and river banks and ocean beaches. Riprap has been placed along the Willamette between the Steel and Broadway bridges below the Willamette Greenway Trail—not a favorable environment for plants and animals.

RiverWalk $2.5 million ALUMINUM pedestrian and bicycle sidewalk opened in mid-2001 across the bottom (railroad) deck of the double-deck Steel Bridge. CANTILEVERED off the south side of the bridge about 25 feet

above the Willamette River, RiverWalk was designed by consulting engineers HNTB of Kansas City. It was constructed by the City of Portland's Office of Transportation to connect with the northern ends of the VERA KATZ EASTBANK ESPLANADE and TOM MCCALL WATERFRONT PARK. RiverWalk, as it is measured across the Steel Bridge's east FIXED SPAN, LIFT SPAN, and west fixed span, is about 780 feet long. A west approach span leading to the bridge proper and located in Tom McCall Park is about 25 feet long. RiverWalk users may also continue on the Eastbank Esplanade, which ends 1.13 miles south.

RiverWalk Railroad Overcrossing An 85-foot-long TRUSS bridge over the main line of the Union Pacific Railroad at the eastern end of RiverWalk. It makes the connection from the STEEL BRIDGE to the east side overlook that leads to the top or highway DECK of the Steel Bridge for those heading west, and to the Rose Quarter, Oregon Convention Center, and Lloyd District for those heading east.

Rivet Metal pin with a head at each end that is passed through a hole to hold pieces of metal together. The head on one end of the rivet is formed once the rivet is through the hole.

Rivet-connected bridges This technology began replacing pin-connected bridges around the end of the 19th century. A four-person riveting crew is called a gang. The heater warms the steel rivets to a bright cherry red and tosses them into a catch pan held by the catcher. Using a pair of tongs and wearing thick gloves, the catcher puts the rivet into an open hole 1/16 of an inch larger than the hot rivet. Next, the bucker-up, using a tool to match the job, places a stop behind the head of the rivet. Last, the riveter hammers on the other end of the hot rivet with a compressed air gun, which expands the rivet to form a head and fill the hole, thus keeping the rivet from falling out. Organized gangs helped install some of the thousands of rivets that hold the Hawthorne Bridge together, as well as other older steel bridges in the Portland area. Riveting technology for bridges became obsolete around 1960, when riveting was replaced by use of high strength bolts, but the process is still used to repair historic bridges all over the United States. The last lower Willamette River bridge built new with rivets was the Morrison Bridge, opened in 1958.

Roadway Part of the bridge that carries highway traffic. Normally the roadway is the top surface of the bridge's DECK. Sidewalks on the bridge may be extensions of the roadway or separate structures.

Ross Island Bridge One of eight FIXED SPAN highway bridges on the last 26 miles of the Willamette River and its Multnomah Channel and one of seven major CANTILEVER TRUSSES in Oregon. Opened in 1926 and designed by GUSTAV LINDENTHAL for Multnomah County, the bridge is now owned and maintained by ODOT. It is a DECK cantilever truss and, with the Marquam Bridge, is an example of this rare type in Oregon. Ross Island's cantilever design is further unusual: most cantilevers have a suspended center span, but Lindenthal omitted this feature on the Ross Island Bridge to achieve maximum height and clearance. Ross Island is one of about 160 steel truss bridges still existing in Oregon. It carries Bull Run water across

the Willamette River in pipes located on its SUPERSTRUCTURE, qualifying it as an AQUEDUCT. (See Abernethy Bridge)

Rust A danger to IRON and STEEL. Rust (also referred to as corrosion) is decay caused by oxidation, or exposure to water and air. Rust causes bits of metal to flake off, eventually weakening the member or structure. The decay process can be faster and more severe for metals unprotected by paint or GALVANIZING. (See CATHODIC PROTECTION, SPALL, TITANIUM, WEATHERING STEEL, and ZINC)

Saddle Saddle-shaped receptacle for the main cable on top of a SUSPENSION BRIDGE TOWER. (See St. Johns Bridge)

St. Johns Bridge One of eight FIXED SPAN highway bridges on the last 26 miles of the Willamette River and its Multnomah Channel. Constructed by Multnomah County and opened in 1931, St. Johns is now owned and maintained by ODOT. It was designed by DAVID STEINMAN of consulting engineers Robinson and Steinman. It is still the only major highway SUSPENSION BRIDGE in the Willamette Valley and one of only three highway bridges of this type in Oregon.

Sauvie Island Bridge Northernmost of eight FIXED SPAN highway bridges on the last 26 miles of the Willamette River and its Multnomah Channel. It crosses the Multnomah Channel of the Willamette near where the Willamette splits at river mile 3. Like the Sellwood Bridge, the 1950 Sauvie Island is a FIXED SPAN TRUSS bridge. The 1950 bridge is being replaced

St. Johns Bridge

Sauvie Island Bridge

with a STEEL TIED ARCH bridge designed by David Evans & Associates for Multnomah County. The new bridge is scheduled to open in 2008. The old bridge has a main span of 200 feet and the new bridge has a main span of 360 feet. The Sauvie Island Bridge is the only vehicular access to the 24,000-acre island it is named after.

Scour Abrasive action of fast-moving water on the soil and rocks around bridge FOUNDATIONS. Scour can undermine a footing and cause the bridge to fail, particularly if there are no PILES to support the FOOTING. One of the most famous bridge failures in Oregon, the collapse of the John Day River Bridge near The Dalles in 1964, was due, in large part, to scour.

Seismic/Seismic Forces/Seismic Retrofit
Seismic refers to something caused by the earth shaking or vibrating. Seismic forces are forces produced in a bridge or other structure by the ground shaking in an earthquake. Prior to the 1990s, the danger of earthquakes in Oregon was considered to be low, and the state's bridges were not designed to withstand large seismic forces. In the 1990s, geologic evidence revealed the possibility of large earthquakes in the Portland area. This indicated a need for seismic retrofit work on existing bridges to lessen the chances of collapse during an earthquake. Seismic retrofit work includes such measures as tying bridge parts together and installing seismic isolators that allow sections of a bridge to move independently without tearing apart. As of 2006, the Marquam and Abernethy bridges, and parts of the Burnside Bridge have been seismically retrofitted. Work on Marquam's

main spans included installation of large seismic isolators imported from Italy.

Sellwood Bridge One of eight FIXED SPAN highway bridges on the last 26 miles of the Willamette River and its Multnomah Channel. Opened in 1925 by Multnomah County, Sellwood's steel four-span CONTINUOUS TRUSS design is credited to GUSTAV LINDENTHAL (main span) and Ira Hedrick (APPROACHES and SUBSTRUCTURE). This is the only four-span continuous truss bridge in Oregon and appears to be an extremely rare bridge type anywhere. Sellwood is made more unusual because it incorporates GIRDERS from the 1894 Burnside Bridge, and landslide has compromised its west end. (See WARREN TRUSS)

Shear Combination of FORCES that causes parallel planes to slide relative to each other. For an example of shear, push your hands together, sliding one against the other. The force required to move your hands is the shearing force. In BEAM bridges, shear works together with TENSION and COMPRESSION to support LOADS applied to the beam. Shear can also refer to the cutting action of two blades moving parallel to each other, like scissors, also called shears.

Sheave Grooved wheel or pulley used to support a rope. Numerous sheaves are used on VERTICAL LIFT BRIDGES. On these bridges, large sheaves support the wire ropes that connect the LIFT SPAN to the COUNTERWEIGHTS. The counterweight sheaves on the HAWTHORNE BRIDGE are nine feet in diameter. On Hawthorne, smaller sheaves carry the operating ropes that pull the lift span up and down.

Simple span Bridge SPAN that is not rigidly connected to adjoining spans. A bridge made up of a series of simple spans may use slightly more material than a CONTINUOUS SPAN BRIDGE. However, the simple spans are easier to design and are less vulnerable to damage due to movement of the supports. Most Portland-area bridges, for example, the Hawthorne Bridge, use simple spans. Exceptions include Abernethy, Sellwood, and Glenn Jackson, all of which use continuous spans.

Single-leaf bascule span BASCULE bridge with one leaf in its LIFT SPAN, which lifts at one end to open and allow passage of traffic. The only known single-leaf bascule bridge in the Portland area is across Willamette Falls Navigational Lock No. 4 at West Linn. (See OVERHEAD COUNTERWEIGHT-TYPE BASCULE)

Slab bridge Type of BEAM BRIDGE in which the ROADWAY DECK itself is designed to act as a wide BEAM. Slab bridges, with their flat bottoms, usually are shorter in length than other bridge types, although they sometimes have spans as long as 80 feet. Slab bridges often are built by joining several PRECAST CONCRETE units together side-by-side.

Spall/Spalling Flaking or chipping of chunks of CONCRETE off the surface of a structure. Spalling is often caused by water working into fine cracks or holes in the CONCRETE. The water can cause spalling by freezing and expanding or by RUSTING the REINFORCING STEEL (also called REBAR),

which causes the steel to expand. In either case, expansion of the frozen water or rusted steel ruptures the concrete and pops it off the structure. Spalling on the BENTS of St. Johns Bridge has exposed metal framing located inside the bents. Spall caused by salt air is particularly destructive. (See CATHODIC PROTECTION)

Span That part of a bridge between two supports. There are single-span bridges and MULTI-SPAN BRIDGES. Span also refers to the distance between supports, and may be used as a noun or verb.

Spandrel In an ARCH BRIDGE with the DECK located above the arch, a spandrel is the space between the arch and deck. (See OPEN SPANDREL)

Specifications Book of rules for building a bridge, building, road, or other project. Specifications include legal and technical requirements the CONTRACTORS must follow. Specifications and PLANS are used together to guide construction of the project.

Springwater Trail Corridor Three Bridges Project Bridges built by the City of Portland and opened in 2006 to carry the Springwater Trail Corridor over Johnson Creek, McLoughlin Boulevard, and the Union Pacific Railroad track in Southeast Portland. Designed by OBEC Consulting Engineers, they are, west to east, a GIRDER, an ARCH, and a TRUSS. The arch over McLoughlin forms a gateway between Portland and Milwaukie. Other arch bridge gateways include the Ross Island and Fremont bridges framing the Willamette River, and the VISTA AVENUE VIADUCT across Southwest Jefferson Street.

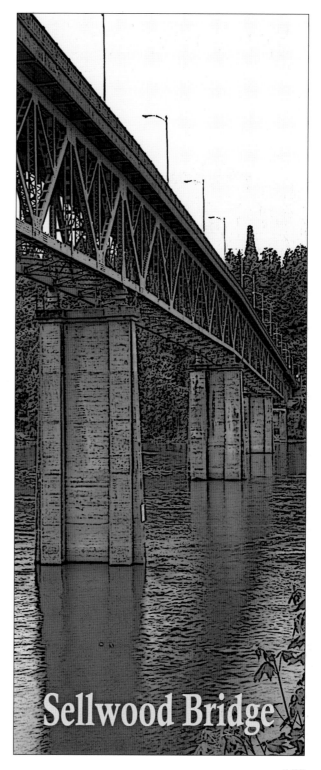

Sellwood Bridge

Starling Pointed clusters of PILINGS protruding from the upriver side of bridges like large knee pads. On the Willamette in Portland, starlings (also called dolphins) can be seen, two each, on the upstream side of the Morrison and Burnside bridges. These additions act as big fenders, preventing ships and river-borne debris such as logs and ice from crashing into and damaging bridge piers. The *Random House Dictionary* notes that the origin of "starling" is unknown and dates to 1675-85.

Steel Metal ALLOY consisting mainly of IRON, plus small amounts of carbon and other ingredients. Steel is more DUCTILE than CAST IRON, and is stronger than WROUGHT IRON. Of the three, steel is better suited for use in bridges and other large structures. Until the middle of the 19th century, steel was expensive and used only to make swords and some tools. During the Industrial Revolution, cheaper and more reliable ways to make steel developed. Modern steel is made to withstand higher STRESSES than the steel used in the 19th century. Steel is now the most commonly used iron alloy in bridge construction. All the large river bridge SUPERSTRUCTURES in the Portland area are made of steel, except the Glenn Jackson Bridge, which is made of CONCRETE. Even the Glenn Jackson uses steel REBAR to reinforce the concrete.

Steel Bridge One of five Portland Central City MOVABLE bridges. This double-deck bridge, named for its material, was designed by Waddell & Harrington for the Oregon-Washington Railway & Navigation Co. (now Union Pacific-Southern Pacific Railroad) so that its lower (railroad) DECK

may be lifted independently, telescoping into the TRUSSES above, or so both decks may be lifted together. This unique combination makes this the only bridge of its type in the world. (See PRATT TRUSS)

Steinman, David (1886-1960) Bridge engineer famous for the Mackinac Bridge (1957) in Michigan, Carquinez Bridge (1927) in California, Henry Hudson Bridge (1936) in New York, and modernizing the Brooklyn Bridge's highway DECK (1948). Steinman designed Portland's St. Johns Bridge, the only SUSPENSION BRIDGE in the Willamette Valley.

Stiffness A measure of how much a structure flexes or deflects under LOAD. Similar to FLEXIBILITY. A stiff structure will flex less than a flexible structure under the same load. (See DEFLECTION)

Strain When a bridge MEMBER has FORCES acting in it because of external LOADS, the member changes length. The change in length is strain. Strain is expressed as a percentage of the original length of the member.

Strauss, Joseph (1870-1938) Bridge designer of more than 400 bridges all over the world, as well as patent-holder for several versions of the Strauss BASCULE. Best known for the Golden Gate Bridge, Strauss is represented in Portland with two spans: Burnside Bridge, designed with a Strauss bascule, and a SINGLE-LEAF OVERHEAD COUNTERWEIGHT-TYPE BASCULE pedestrian bridge across Willamette Falls Navigational Lock No. 4 at West Linn. Strauss's largest contribution to the Pacific Northwest is the massive 1.6-mile-long CANTILEVER TRUSS Lewis and Clark Bridge (formerly the

Longview Bridge), dating to 1930, across the Columbia River between Rainier, Oregon and Longview, Washington.

Strength Ability of structures to carry LOADS. Railroad bridges, for example, are designed stronger than highway bridges. Railroad bridges can carry diesel locomotives weighing up to 200 tons, while highway trucks weigh up to 50 tons.

Stress FORCE divided by area, as in pounds per square inch. By the mid-1800s, ENGINEERS understood the amount of stress in bridges caused by the LOADS from 40-ton locomotives and were able to conduct tests and use measuring instruments to determine safety factors in bridge design. Types of stresses are TENSION, COMPRESSION, and SHEAR.

Stringer One of a series of BEAMS that directly support a bridge DECK. Stringers usually run lengthwise with the bridge and are supported by FLOORBEAMS running crosswise across the bridge. Bridge stringers may be made of WOOD, CONCRETE, STEEL, or other materials.

Structure Materials or parts assembled in a way to support LOADS or FORCES. Structures can be made by people, such as bridges and dams, or they can be part of nature, for example, trees and skeletons.

Structural art Art form arising from the Industrial Revolution and the use of IRON and later STEEL and REINFORCED CONCRETE. It is parallel to and independent of architecture, and is defined as forms designed out of an ENGINEER'S imagination to control natural forces in an elegant

way. Examples include Brooklyn Bridge, Eiffel Tower, St. Louis Arch, Hell Gate Bridge, and other personality-driven works such as Portland's Fremont, Oregon City, and St. Johns bridges, as well as Oregon's McCullough bridges. See *The Tower and the Bridge, The New Art of Structural Engineering*, by David Billington; *Bridges, Long Spans of North America*, by David Plowden, and *The Sense of Beauty, Being the Outline of Aesthetic Theory*, by George Santayana.

Substructure That part of a bridge supporting and carrying the weight of the SUPERSTRUCTURE to the ground. Bridge substructures are assemblies of components such as PIERS, BENTS, FOOTINGS, CAISSONS, and PILES. Substructures differ widely from bridge to bridge due to variations in ground conditions, bridge heights, and superstructure designs.

Superstructure Horizontal portion of a bridge that spans between the supports, or SUBSTRUCTURE. The superstructure carries the traffic and passes the weight of the traffic and superstructure to the substructure. ARCH, BEAM, TRUSS, SUSPENSION, CABLE-STAYED, and MOVABLE BRIDGES are varieties of bridge superstructures.

Suspenders Wire ropes or CABLES that support a bridge DECK by suspending it from the main support structure overhead. On SUSPENSION BRIDGES such as the St. Johns, the suspenders hang from the main cables that are draped between the TOWERS. The Fremont Bridge also uses suspender ropes to hang the DECK off the ARCH in the center portion over the river, as does the new Sauvie Island Bridge arch (2008).

Suspension bridge One of three main bridge types, along with ARCH and BEAM/TRUSS bridges. On a suspension bridge, the weight of the ROADWAY DECK and traffic is supported by main CABLES draped over TOWERS in a CATENARY- or PARABOLIC-shaped curve. The deck typically is connected to the main cables by SUSPENDERS. The main cables are tied to the ground by ANCHORAGES. ENGINEERS have looked to this bridge type to span wide spaces since the mid-1800s. Suspension bridges are expensive and can take a long time to build. Two of the most famous suspension bridges are the Brooklyn Bridge in New York and the Golden Gate Bridge at San Francisco. The longest suspension bridge in the U.S. is the Verazanno Narrows Bridge in New York City. There are only three major highway suspension bridges in Oregon: the St. Johns Bridge in Portland and two smaller bridges at Lake Billy Chinook in Central Oregon.

Swing bridge One of three main movable bridge types, along with VERTICAL LIFT and BASCULE. A swing bridge opens by rotating its span on a center PIER located in the waterway. Several early Portland-area bridges included swing spans. All of the swing spans have been replaced except two railroad bridges across the Oregon Slough and the Columbia River. (See Railroad Bridges) Swing bridges are outdated now because they restrict the waterway for ship passage and they are slow to open and close. A rare asymmetrical swing bridge opened in 1993 near a navigational lock at Bonneville Dam.

Synchronous horizontal/vertical excitation Terms used to describe the excessive swaying or bouncing of some pedestrian bridges, including the London Millennium Bridge opened across the Thames in London in 2000. The first modern CABLE-STAYED BRIDGE opened in Europe in the mid-1800s. During the opening ceremony, a marching band swayed the bridge until it collapsed. Stories from ancient times claim that soldiers marching in step could cause a bridge to collapse. (See EXCITE THE MOLECULES and GALLOPING GERTIE).

Tension/Tensile force Force that tends to make something longer, or to pull it apart. While a tension or tensile force lengthens or pulls apart, a COMPRESSION or COMPRESSIVE FORCE makes something shorter or pushes it together. On SUSPENSION BRIDGES, the main CABLES and SUSPENDER ropes work in tension.

Through truss bridge Bridge with the traffic roadway DECK located between the trusses. When the roadway deck is on top of the truss, it is called a DECK TRUSS bridge. Broadway Bridge and BNSF Railway Bridge 5.1 are through trusses, while Hawthorne and Steel bridges are through trusses with additional traffic lanes outside their trusses. Marquam Bridge, with two traffic decks, is a combination deck truss and through truss.

Thrust Pushing FORCE or pressure exerted by a structure or on a structure. For example, the downward and outward force exerted by an ARCH at each end.

Tied arch ARCH BRIDGE designed like an archer's bow, with the "string" (or tie) connecting one end to the other. This arrangement holds the ARCH in COMPRESSION and the tie in TENSION. Tied arches are used at sites where it is not feasible to support the arch horizontally at ground level. The tie carries the horizontal THRUST that would otherwise act on the ABUTMENTS. (See Fremont Bridge, UNION STATION PEDESTRIAN BRIDGE, and 2008 Sauvie Island Bridge)

Titanium Lustrous, hard, lightweight metal that is rust-resistant. ODOT has experimented with coating titanium on a section of the Depot Bay Bridge on the Oregon Coast to determine its efficiency for preventing rust as compared to ZINC coating. (See CATHODIC PROTECTION and GALVANIZING)

Torsion Combination of FORCES that can be described as twisting. As an example, grasp the ends of a thin flat piece of plastic or wood and twist the ends in opposite directions. The forces that make the material twist are torsional. Another example of torsion is the turning force required to twist a drill into a piece of wood. Torsion is produced in bridges by uneven GRAVITY or wind LOADS on the DECK. The torsion on GALLOPING GERTIE (first Tacoma Narrows Bridge) was caused by wind pushing and lifting the bridge deck.

Toughness Ability of a material to withstand harsh treatment such as sudden impacts without breaking. Toughness of a material is related to how DUCTILE or BRITTLE it is. Some types of STEEL are made tougher by special treatment when the steel is made at the steel mill.

Tower Tall PIER or frame supporting the main CABLES of a SUSPENSION BRIDGE or the inclined cables of a CABLE-STAYED BRIDGE. Most bridge towers have been built of STEEL. However, some early SUSPENSION BRIDGES, such as the Brooklyn Bridge, used stone. In recent times, some suspension and most cable-stayed bridges use CONCRETE towers.

Transportation Management Operations Center (TMOC) Since 1 January 1996, keeping traffic moving has been the responsibility of ODOT's TMOC. Located at Region One in Northwest Portland, the center is staffed 365 days a year, 24 hours a day and responds to and tracks traffic in Multnomah, Clackamas, Washington, Hood River, and Columbia counties. TMOC is equipped with an elaborate computer system that governs variable message signs and video cameras (more than 100 mounted on highways and bridges in the Portland metropolitan area), and uses enhanced traffic control devices such as ramp meters and paging systems. TMOC also directs Incident Response vehicles. Drivers patrol the highways, ready to help motorists who have run out of gas or need a tire changed. To check conditions, travelers may dial 511 or go online <www.tripcheck.com>.

Triangle Three-cornered or three-sided figure. Triangles, among the strongest structures in the world, are found everywhere, even between pieces of the thinnest cardboard. TRUSSES are made of a series of triangles connected together.

Triggering event Term for a catastrophic, accidental or deliberate event, either natural or political, which changes

Trunnion Large shaft or axle carrying a SHEAVE or other moving part in MOVABLE BRIDGES. The trunnions supporting the COUNTERWEIGHT SHEAVES in the Hawthorne Bridge are 12 inches in diameter and four feet long. Trunnions are also used in the hinge assemblies supporting BASCULE BRIDGE lift spans as they open and close. The main trunnions carrying the Burnside Bridge's lift span are 28 inches in diameter and eight feet long. The main trunnions carrying the Morrison Bridge's lift span are 24 inches in diameter and more than seven feet long.

Truss Framework made up of MEMBERS arranged in a series of TRIANGLES. Truss members in bridges are called CHORDS, DIAGONALS, and POSTS.

Truss bridge A truss bridge is a form of BEAM BRIDGE, except that trusses are made up of smaller members. (Imagine a solid beam of steel with some of the steel cut away to leave a framework with triangular openings.) For a given SPAN and LOAD, truss bridges are lighter than solid-beam bridges. Thus it is practical to build truss bridges with longer spans than solid-beam bridges. The world's longest-span truss bridge is the Quebec Bridge, opened in 1917 with a MAIN SPAN of 1,800 feet. Truss bridges also are useful for spans of moderate length. All MOVABLE BRIDGES in the Portland area are STEEL truss bridges, as are most of the area's larger FIXED SPAN bridges. (See "Common Historic Truss Designs" in appendices.) Truss bridges, once popular,

are declining in number. In 2006, there are only about 160 steel truss highway bridges known to remain in Oregon (out of about 6,700 highway bridges total). (See PARKER TRUSS, PENNSYLVANIA-PETIT TRUSS, PRATT TRUSS, and WARREN TRUSS)

Union Station Pedestrian Bridge Pedestrian and bicycle bridge opened in March 2000 across the railroad tracks between Portland Union Train Station and River District in Northwest Portland. Owned by the City of Portland, it was designed by KPFF Consulting Engineers and ZGF Architects as a TIED ARCH. It is an extremely FLEXIBLE bridge, and an excellent place to EXCITE THE MOLECULES. (See Fremont Bridge)

Vera Katz Eastbank Esplanade $32.5 million City of Portland project designed by Mayer-Reed Landscape Architects to enhance the Central City waterfront. Opened in 2001 between I-5 and the east bank of the Willamette River, this linear "transportation connector" for walkers and bicyclists extends 1.13 miles south from the Steel Bridge. The Esplanade, renamed the Vera Katz Eastbank Esplanade in 2004 to honor Portland Mayor Vera Katz, contains several bridges, among them a 1,300-foot-long FLOATING BRIDGE, one of only a half dozen places a person can stoop to touch the Willamette River in downtown Portland. At its northern end, an ALUMINUM sidewalk called RiverWalk is cantilevered off the bottom (railroad) deck of the Steel Bridge to carry people across the Willamette River. At this northern juncture, the Esplanade also connects with the RIVERWALK RAILROAD OVERCROSSING, an 85-foot-long TRUSS bridge leading bicyclists

and pedestrians to the Rose Quarter District, or to the upper (highway) deck of the Steel Bridge.

Vertical Up and down direction at right angles to the earth. (The opposite of HORIZONTAL, a sideways direction level or flat with the earth). For example, a pop bottle standing straight up is vertical, true also of telephone poles, trees, and human beings. VERTICAL LIFT BRIDGES like the Hawthorne, Steel, and Interstate bridges operate with COUNTERWEIGHTS and DECKS that move straight up and down, or in a vertical direction.

Vertical lift bridge One of three main movable bridge types, along with SWING and BASCULE. A vertical lift bridge has a LIFT SPAN that can be raised up and down so watercraft can pass. The lift span is raised and kept level by a system of synchronized machinery and COUNTERWEIGHTS similar to an elevator. (See Hawthorne, Steel, and Interstate bridges)

Veterans Hospital Pedestrian Skybridge Combination TRUSS and CABLE-STAYED BRIDGE, this long (almost two football fields long) pedestrian-only bridge carries patients, visitors, medical staff, and equipment 170 feet above the canyon between the Veterans Hospital and Oregon Health & Science University South. It was designed by KPFF Consulting Engineers and opened in 1992. Because of space restrictions, it was erected from the bridge's two tall structural towers out, or by the CANTILEVER method. It has two separate support systems. The cable stays on each end are strong enough to support the DEAD

LOAD, but not the full live LOAD. They help keep the bridge from excessive swaying during windy weather. With enough people walking in step or jumping together, you can easily EXCITE THE MOLECULES on this bridge. (See SYNCHRONOUS HORIZONTAL/VERTICAL EXCITATION)

Viaduct Bridge over land, usually with multiple short or medium-length SPANS. Several viaducts on the east side of the Willamette River carry city streets over railroad tracks and industrial areas. These viaducts include the north end of McLoughlin Boulevard and the approaches to Morrison and Hawthorne bridges.

Vista Avenue Viaduct Multiple-span CONCRETE VIADUCT built in 1926 across S.W. Jefferson Street in Portland. The main span is a 248-foot OPEN SPANDREL ARCH. It is owned by the city and is listed as a Portland Landmark by the Portland Historic Landmarks Commission.

Waddell, John Alexander Low (1854-1938) ENGINEER and inventor of the modern day VERTICAL LIFT BRIDGE. Waddell was the designer of the Halsted Street Bridge (1895) in Chicago, City Waterway Bridge (1913) in Tacoma, Washington, Arroyo Seco Bridge (1913) in Los Angeles (part of the nation's first freeway), and others. The firm of Waddell & Harrington designed three Portland-area vertical lift bridges: Hawthorne, Steel, and the northbound Interstate. In Portland, another Waddell & Harrington bridge is

the STEEL GIRDER structure built in 1910 and now carrying N.E. 12th Avenue over the I-84 freeway, MAX light rail track, and Union Pacific Railroad.

Warren truss Type of TRUSS with MEMBERS that form a series of TRIANGLES with alternating "A" and "V" shapes. The Warren truss dates to 1848. Lower Willamette River bridges with Warren trusses include Sellwood, Ross Island, Marquam, Burnside, St. Johns, and the 1950 Sauvie Island. (See PARKER TRUSS, PENNSYLVANIA-PETIT TRUSS, and PRATT TRUSS)

Weathering steel Type of STEEL made with additives that produce a permanent coat of RUST. The tight rust coat does not flake off, protecting the underlying steel from air and water (oxidation). This means weathering steel does not need to be painted, and so is less expensive to maintain during the life of a structure. The lift span and towers of the BNSF Railway 5.1 Bridge across the Willamette River are made of weathering steel, easily recognized because of their dark red, rusty color. (The bridge's side spans, erected 80 years earlier and not made of weathering steel, are painted silver.) The ARCH SPAN in the new Sauvie Island Bridge (2008) is also made of weathering steel.

Weld/Welding Method of joining pieces of metal by heating the edges until they melt and mix. When the edges cool, a solid connection forms called a joint. Part of the welding process involves adding metal to

fill the gap between the two pieces. A good place to see bridge welds is on the UNION STATION PEDESTRIAN BRIDGE. The tie girders, one on each side running the length of the walkway on the outside of the bridge, show many welds.

Wood Until the 1800s, the only materials commonly used for bridge building were wood and stone. Wood, also called "timber," is moderately strong both in TENSION and COMPRESSION. Wood fell out of favor for bridge building because of its impermanence—it rots, burns easily, and insects eat it. Today's wooden bridges last longer because the wood is chemically treated. Compressing and gluing pieces of wood together, called laminating, makes the wood stronger.

Wrought iron IRON ALLOY with a low carbon content, thus extremely pure. Wrought iron is not as BRITTLE as cast iron and can be easily WELDED. Wrought iron was used extensively for bridge construction in the 19th century before STEEL became widely used because of its higher strength. For example, parts of the 1894 Burnside Bridge and other first generation Portland bridges were made of wrought iron.

Zinc Metal used to thinly coat STEEL or IRON to protect the steel or iron from being attacked by water and air. This coating process is called GALVANIZING. Water RUSTS iron and steel unless they are protected by galvanizing or paint. (See CATHODIC PROTECTION, SPALL, TITANIUM, and WEATHERING STEEL).

PORTLAND TRANSPORTATION HISTORY TIMELINE

1853 – First ferry in Portland (Stark Street)

1857 – Construction begins on a plank road (Canyon Road) connecting Portland to the Tualatin Plains

1868 – Oregon Central Railroad breaks ground

1872–1884 – Railroad construction peaks

1872 – First horse drawn-trolleys

1887 – First bridge across Willamette River (Morrison)

1888 – First Steel Bridge opens

1890 – First electric streetcar goes into service

1891 – Madison Bridge #1 opens at the future site of the Hawthorne Bridge

1896 – Union Station opens

1900 – Madison Bridge #2 opens at site of Madison Bridge #1

1905 – Second Morrison Bridge opens

1905 – Balch Gulch Bridge opens for the Lewis & Clark Exposition and World's Fair

1909 – Portland-Seattle railroad completed

1910 – Hawthorne Bridge opens, replacing Madison #2

1912 – New Steel Bridge opens, replacing old bridge

1912 – Peak of streetcar system

1913 – Broadway Bridge opens

1913 – First traffic signal (5th and Washington)

1917 – Interstate Bridge across the Columbia opens

1925 – Sellwood Bridge opens

1926 – Burnside Bridge, Ross Island Bridge, and Vista Avenue Viaduct open

1927 – Lovejoy Viaduct opens off the west end of the Broadway Bridge

1927 – Swan Island Airport begins service

1929 – Harbor wall construction begins

1931 – Burnside Street widening project

1931 – St. Johns Bridge opens,

1933 – Barbur Boulevard opens

1941 – Portland Columbia Airport begins service

1942 – Harbor Drive construction begins (completed after WWII)

1950 – Last streetcar goes out of service

1950 – Sauvie Island Bridge opens, last Portland-area ferry out of business

1958 – Interurban rail service between Oregon City and Portland suspended

1958 – Southbound Interstate Bridge opens

1958 – New (third) Morrison Bridge opens

1966 – Marquam Bridge opens, completing Interstate 5 through Portland

1969 – TriMet forms

1972 – Downtown Plan adopted

1973 – Portland's first bike plan is developed

1905 Morrison Bridge.

Walking the Fremont Bridge, People's Day 1973.

1973 – Fremont Bridge (I-405) opens, completing downtown freeway loop

1974 – Harbor Drive removed to make way for Tom McCall Waterfront Park

1975 – Downtown Parking and Circulation Policy adopted

1976 – Mt. Hood Freeway withdrawn from Interstate System, funds diverted to Banfield Light Rail Transit and 140 other highway and transit projects

1977 – Downtown transit mall opens

1986 – Eastside MAX light rail opens, renewing rail passenger service in Portland

1987 – Willamette Shore Trolley (Oregon Electric Railway) begins operating along vacated Southern Pacific Railroad right-of-way between RiverPlace and Lake Oswego

1988 – Central City Plan adopted

1989 – BNSF Railway Bridge 5.1 main span switched from swing to vertical lift

1989 – TriMet named "America's Best Large Transit Agency" by American Public Transit Association

1991 – Replicas of Council Crest cars arrive and Vintage Trolley service begins between Lloyd Center and downtown Portland

1993 – SamTrak Excursion Train begins operating between OMSI and Sellwood

1995 – Central City Transportation Management Plan adopted

1995 – Portland selected as the most bicycle friendly city in the U.S. by *Bicycling Magazine*

1996 – Bicycle Master Plan adopted and the Transportation Management Association formed

1998 – Westside MAX light rail opens between Portland and Hillsboro

1999 – Lovejoy Viaduct removed from Broadway Bridge

2001 – Airport MAX Red Line opens between downtown Portland and Portland International Airport

2001 – Portland Streetcar opens between Portland State University (PSU) and Pearl District

2001 – Union Station Pedestrian Bridge opens

2001 – Eastbank Esplanade opens with a floating bridge, RiverWalk Railroad Overcrossing Bridge, and RiverWalk (Steel Bridge) pedestrian walkway

2003 – SamTrak Excursion Train stops running

2004 – Interstate Max Yellow Line opens between Portland and the Exposition Center

2005 – Portland Streetcar extended from PSU to RiverPlace

2006 – Construction begins to extend MAX along the Downtown Transit Mall between PSU and Union Train Station

2006 – Springwater Corridor Trail Three Bridges bicycle and pedestrian crossings open

2006 – Portland Streetcar extended from RiverPlace to S.W. Gibbs Street

2006 – Portland Aerial Tram opens

2007 – Portland Streetcar extended from S.W. Gibbs to S.W. Lowell Street

2008 – Second Sauvie Island Bridge opens

2009 – Downtown Transit Mall reconstruction extends MAX from PSU to Union Train Station

From City of Portland Office of Transportation's "Portland Transportation History Timeline," TriMet's "A History of Public Transit in Portland," and website of the Willamette Shore Trolley

BRIDGE OWNERS AND OTHER BRIDGE RESOURCES

America Society of Civil Engineers, History and Heritage Committee: This standing committee of the American Society of Civil Engineers, headquartered in Reston, Virginia, considers nominations for Historic Civil Engineering Landmarks, both national and international, and recommends qualifying projects to the ASCE Board of Directors. Each approved landmark is marked with a plaque recognizing the project and describing its significance. The committee was established in 1964. There are 240 Historic Civil Engineering Landmarks in 2006, of which 69 are bridges. Oregon is home to three landmarks: Bonneville Dam, Columbia River Scenic Highway, and the Rogue River Bridge at Gold Beach. Former ASCE President and engineer John Alexander Low Waddell designed the 1912 Armour-Swift-Burlington Bridge, in Kansas City, Missouri, listed as a landmark in 1996. Waddell, one of the late 19th-early 20th century's top bridge engineers, designed three Portland-area bridges. A complete list of landmarks is maintained on the ASCE web site.

> American Society of Civil Engineers
> History and Heritage Committee
> 1801 Alexander Bell Drive
> Reston, VA 20191-4400
> (800) 548-2723
> <www.asce.org>

Burlington Northern Santa Fe (BNSF) Railway: owns and maintains three major railroad bridges across rivers in the Portland area: Bridge 5.1, across the Willamette River (vertical lift); Bridge 8.8, across the Oregon Slough (swing span); and Bridge 9.6, across the Columbia River (swing span). BNSF owns other area bridges, among them Lombard Street, Fessenden Street, and Willamette Blvd. highway overcrossings.

> Manager of Bridges and Buildings
> 5324 E. Trent Road
> Spokane, WA 99212
> <www.bnsf.com>

City of Portland: owns and maintains about 150 highway and pedestrian bridges, but only two dozen cross water, for example, Johnson Creek, Fanno Creek, and the Columbia Slough. Among the major city-owned highway bridges are Balch Gulch and Vista Avenue Viaduct. PDOT's RiverWalk pedestrian and bicycle sidewalk opened across the Steel Bridge in 2001. Three large pedestrian bridges, a project of Portland Parks & Recreation, opened along the western end of the Springwater Trail Corridor in 2006. A city-built tramway (3,300-foot-long "aerial" bridge) opens early 2007.

> Bureau of Engineering and Development
> Bridges and Structures Section
> 1120 S.W. 5th, #814
> Portland, OR 97204
> (503) 823-7063
> <www.portlandonline.com/transportation>

Clackamas County: owns and maintains 168 bridges, including the oldest bridges in the state, the Dodge Park (Lusted Road) and Bull Run bridges. Clackamas County also owns one "floating bridge," the Canby Ferry.

> Bridge Section, Clackamas County Dept. of Transportation
> 902 Abernethy Road
> Oregon City, OR 97045
> (503) 650-3990
> E-mail: bridgeshop@co.clackamas.or.us
> <www.co.clackamas.or.us>

Covered Bridge Society of Oregon: formed in 1978, with 175 members in 2006. Dues are $15 a year and pay for notices of monthly meetings and *The Bridge Tender* newsletter, published four times a year.

> Jeannine Schmeltzer, Secretary-Treasurer
> 24595 S.W. Neill Road
> Sherwood, OR 97140
> (503) 628-1906

Federal Highway Administration (FHWA): part of the U.S. Department of Transportation. All public highway bridges in the U.S. must be inspected for safety every two years. FHWA works through state departments of transportation to administer and enforce biennial checks of the nation's 586,930 highway bridges 20 feet and longer.

Oregon Division Office, Federal Highway Administration
530 Center St., N.E. #100
Salem, OR 97301
(503) 399-5749
<www.fhwa.dot.gov>

Historic American Engineering Record (HAER): a branch of the National Park Service, United States Department of Interior. Located in Washington, D.C., HAER is a national archive of drawings, photographs, and histories of America's engineering and industrial sites, including historic bridges. Since 1969, teams of architects, historians, photographers, and engineers have documented more than 1,000 bridges in the U.S. for the Historic American Building Survey/ Historic American Engineering Record/Historic American Landscapes Survey collection at the Library of Congress. These teams produce the documentation for projects such as the Willamette River Bridges study of 1999, which are placed in the Library of Congress as a public record.

Historic American Engineering Record, National Park Service
U.S. Department of the Interior
1849 C Street, 2270
Washington, D.C. 20240
(202) 354-2186
<www.cr.nps.gov/habshaer/haer/>

Multnomah County: maintains and owns 30 bridges and approaches between the Willamette River and Cascade Locks, most spans in the eastern half of Multnomah County. The County's largest bridges are the bridges across the Willamette River: Broadway, Burnside, Morrison, Hawthorne, and Sellwood bridges, and, across the Multnomah Channel of the Willamette River, the Sauvie Island Bridge.

Multnomah County Transportation Division, Bridge Section
1403 S.E. Water Ave.
Portland, OR 97214
(503) 988-3757
<www.co.multnomah.or.us/bridge/index.htm>

National Register of Historic Places: under the domain of the National Park Service, keeper of the list of the nation's cultural resources worthy of preservation. This list contains districts, historic and archeological sites, buildings, bridges, and objects of national, state, and local significance. As a result of a Programmatic Agreement signed in 2006 between the Oregon Department of Transportation and the State Historic Preservation Office (see SHPO below), nine Portland-area bridges across the Willamette River, Multnomah Channel of the Willamette River, and the Columbia River are eligible for or listed in the National Register of Historic Places: Interstate (1917), Sauvie Island (1950), St. Johns, Broadway, Steel, Burnside, Hawthorne, Ross Island, and the Oregon City Arch.

National Register Coordinator for Oregon
State Historic Preservation Office
Oregon Parks and Recreation Department
725 Summer Street N.E., Suite C
Salem OR 97301
(503) 986-0684
<www.oregonheritage.org>

Oregon Department of Transportation (ODOT): owns 2,650 bridges, which includes all Oregon's interstate and intrastate highway bridges. The following ODOT bridges are featured in *The Portland Bridge Book*: Glenn L. Jackson and Interstate (Columbia River), Abernethy (I-205), Fremont, Marquam, Oregon City, Ross Island, St. Johns, and Steel top deck (Willamette). Until 1999, when the Oregon legislature stopped the funding, ODOT took care of the state's covered bridges restoration and maintenance program. ODOT administers the biennial federal highway bridge inspection program for all Oregon bridges and, for certain spans, splits maintenance responsibilities with cities and counties for surface repair, snow removal, and drainage problems.

Local Agency Bridge Coordinator
Bridge Engineering Section
355 Capitol Street, N.E.
Salem, OR 97301-3871
(503) 986-3401
<www.oregon.gov/Odot/hwy/bridge/>

Oregon Department of Transportation's Geo-Environmental Section: The section, part of the Technical Services Branch, is responsible for all types of natural and cultural resources research and evaluation, and for ensuring environmental regulatory compliance for proposed transportation projects. The Cultural Resources program, part of the Environmental Planning Unit, evaluates the significance of Oregon's historic bridges to ensure appropriate protection. It has recently completed a comprehensive Bridges Preservation Plan.

Oregon Department of Transportation
Geo-Environmental Section
355 Capitol Street N.E.
Salem, OR 97301
<www.oregon.gov/ODOT/HWY/GEOENVIRONMENTAL/>

Oregon State Historic Preservation Office (SHPO): consults with state and federal agencies to avoid or mitigate the loss of significant historic resources. Also see the National Register of Historic Places. In the case of the Willamette River bridges, SHPO works with the Oregon Department of Transportation through ODOT's Geo-Environmental Section.

Oregon Parks & Recreation Dept. Heritage Programs:
State Historic Preservation Office
725 Summer Street N.E. Suite C
Salem, OR 97301
(503) 986-0677
<www.oregon.gov/OPRD/HCD/SHPO/index.shtml>

Society for Industrial Archeology (SIA): encourages the study, interpretation, and preservation of historically significant industrial sites, structures, artifacts, and technology. Formed in 1971, SIA is a forum on the working past in which people share knowledge about the structures and sites of our industrial heritage. The Society also seeks to raise awareness among communities, public agencies, and property owners about the advantages of preserving the landscapes, structures, and equipment significant in the history of technology, engineering, and industry, through continued or adaptive re-use. "Archeology" in the name signifies SIA's concern with tangible evidence. Each year, in different cities or regions with a significant legacy of industrial activity, the Society holds its late-spring Annual Conference, and a Fall Tour in another location. Central to these gatherings are special tours of contemporary and historic industrial sites and processes. All SIA members receive *IA, The Journal of*

the Society for Industrial Archeology, the "Society for Industrial Archeology Newsletter," and discounts in fees for annual meetings, fall tours, and occasional events. The SIA welcomes members with a wide range of professional and avocational interests in industrial archeology.

Don Durfee
Society for Industrial Archeology
Department of Social Sciences
Michigan Technological University
1400 Townsend Drive
Houghton, MI 49931-1295
(906) 487-1889
E-mail: sia@mtu.edu

Union Pacific Railroad: owns the Steel Bridge, running, in 2006, seven Amtrak trains and 10-15 freight trains a day across the bridge's bottom deck. MAX (482 daily crossings), highway traffic, pedestrians, and bicyclists use the Steel's top deck. (For information about RiverWalk, the pedestrian and bicycle walkway on Steel's bottom deck, see Steel Bridge chapter or the glossary). Union Pacific also owns the railroad bridge at Lake Oswego formerly owned by Southern Pacific Railroad.

Manager of Bridge Maintenance
Union Pacific Railroad
PO Box 1358
Eugene, OR 97440
(541) 341-5630
<www.uprr.com>

Washington County: owns and maintains about 140 bridges, of which 70 percent are timber bridges with concrete or steel in their spans. Washington County maintains Scholls Ferry Road Bridge (near Washington Square) and the 660-foot-long Rood Bridge, Washington County's longest span.

Washington County Operations Division
Land Use and Transportation
1400 S.W. Walnut St.
Hillsboro, OR 97213
(503) 846-7623
<www.co.Washington.or.us>

Willamette Light Brigade: volunteer-led non-profit citizens group working to add architectural lighting to the bridges across the Willamette River in Portland—to make these unique structures visible by night as well as by day, and to add an element to the riverfront and river crossings. WLB continues to solicit assistance to meet its goals.

Paddy Tillet, Chair
PO Box 40390
Portland, OR 97214
(503) 224-1454 or 235-8384

BIBLIOGRAPHY

BOOKS

Abbott, Carl. *The Great Extravaganza: Portland and the Lewis and Clark Exposition.* Portland: Oregon Historical Society Press, 1991.

————. *Greater Portland: Urban Life and Landscape in the Pacific Northwest.* Philadelphia: University of Pennsylvania Press, 2001.

————. *Portland, Gateway to the Northwest.* Northridge, California: Windsor Books, 1985.

————. *Portland, Planning, Politics, and Growth in a Twentieth-Century City.* Lincoln, Nebraska: University of Nebraska Press, 1983.

Battaile, Connie Hopkins. *The Oregon Book, Information A to Z.* Newport, Oregon: Saddle Mountain Press, 1998.

Beckett, Derrick. *Bridges, Great Buildings of the World.* New York: Hamlyn Publishing Group, 1969.

Bill, Max. *Robert Maillart.* Erlenbach-Zürich: Verlag für Architektur AG, 1949.

Billington, David P. *Robert Maillart's Bridges: The Art of Engineering.* Princeton, New Jersey: Princeton University Press, 1979.

————. *The Tower and the Bridge.* New York: Basic Books, 1983.

Bobrick, Benson. *Parsons Brinckerhoff: The First 100 Years.* New York: Van Nostrand Reinhold, 1985.

Bosker, Gideon and Lena Lencek. *Frozen Music: A History of Portland Architecture.* Portland, Oregon: Western Imprints (Oregon Historical Society Press), 1989.

Brangwyn, Frank and Christian Barman. *The Bridge.* New York: Dodd, Mead & Co., 1926.

Brown, David J. *Bridges.* New York: MacMillan, 1993.

Brown, Kathi Ann. *Diversity by Design, Celebrating Seventy-Five Years of Howard Needles Tammen & Bergendoff (1914-1989).* Kansas City: Lowell Press, 1989.

California Department of Transportation. *Historic Highway Bridges of California.* California Department of Transportation, 1990.

Cassady, Stephen. *Spanning the Gate.* Mill Valley, California: Squarebooks, 1979.

Condit, Carl W. *American Building Art 19th Century.* New York: Oxford University Press, 1960.

————. *American Building Art 20th Century.* New York: Oxford University Press, 1961.

Cornerstones of Community: Buildings of Portland's African American History, revised and expanded. Portland, Oregon: Bosco-Milligan Foundation, Architectural Heritage Center, 1997.

Cortright, Robert. *Bridging, Discovering the Beauty of Bridges.* Tigard, Oregon: Bridge Ink, 1998.

————. *Bridging the World.* Wilsonville, Oregon: Bridge Ink, 2003.

Culp, Edwin D. *Stations West: The Story of the Oregon Railways.* Caldwell, Idaho: Caxton, 1972.

DeLony, Eric. *Landmark American Bridges.* New York: American Society of Civil Engineers, 1992.

————. *Gustav Lindenthal.* American National Biography, vol. 13. New York: Oxford University Press, 1999.

Dillon, Richard, Thomas Moulin, and Don DeNevi. *High Steel: Building the Bridges Across San Francisco Bay.* Berkeley, California: Celestial Arts, 1979.

Dodds, Gordon B. *The American Northwest, A History of Oregon and Washington.* Arlington Heights, Illinois: Forum Press, 1986.

Dunn, Jon L. *National Geographic Field Guide to the Birds of North America.* Washington, D.C.: National Geographic, 1999.

Egan, Ferol. *Fremont: Explorer for a Restless Nation.* Garden City, New York: Doubleday, 1977.

Fisher, Douglas A. *Steel Serves the Nation, 1901-1951: The Fifty Year Story of United States Steel.* New York: United States Steel Corporation, 1951.

Gardner, Wilmer, ed. *Old Oregon City,* 2nd edition. Oregon City, Oregon: Clackamas County Historical Society, 1987.

Gaston, Joseph. *Centennial History of Oregon.* Chicago: S.J. Clarke, 1912.

Gideon, Sigfried. *Space, Time and Architecture,* 5th edition revised. Cambridge: Harvard University Press, 1967.

Gies, Joseph. *Bridges and Men.* Garden City, New York: Doubleday, 1963.

Gotchy, Joe. *Bridging the Narrows.* Gig Harbor, Washington: Peninsula Historical Society, 1990.

Hidy, Ralph W., et al. *The Great Northern Railway, a History.* Boston, Massachusetts: Harvard Business School Press, 1988.

Holstine, Craig and Richard Hobbs. *Spanning Washington: Historic Highway Bridges of the Evergreen State.* Pullman, Washington: Washington State University Press, 2005.

Hool, George A. and W.S. Kinne, eds. *Movable and Long-Span Steel Bridges.* New York: McGraw Hill, 1943.

Hopkins, H.J. *A Span of Bridges.* Devon: David & Charles-Newton Abbott, 1970.

Houck, Michael and M.J. Cody, eds. *Wild in the City: a Guide to Portland's Natural Areas.* Portland: Oregon Historical Society Press, 2001.

Hovey, Otis Ellis. *Movable Bridges.* Vol. 1. New York: John Wiley & Sons, 1926.

Jackson, Donald C. *Great American Bridges and Dams.* Washington, D.C.: Preservation Press, 1988.

Kemp, Emory and Beverly B. Fluty. *The Wheeling Suspension Bridge: A Pictorial Heritage.* Charleston, West Virginia: Pictorial Histories Publishing Co., 1999.

Kidney, Walter C. *Pittsburgh's Bridges: Architecture and Engineering.* Pittsburgh: Pittsburgh History & Landmarks Foundation, 1999.

Kranakis, Eda. *Constructing a Bridge: An Exploration of Engineering Culture, Design, and Research in Nineteenth-Century France and America.* Cambridge and London: MIT Press, 1997.

Kunhardt, Philip B., ed. *Life: The First Fifty Years.* New York: Little Brown, 1986.

Labbe, John T. *Fares, Please!* Caldwell, Idaho: Caxton, 1980.

Levy, Matthys and Mario Salvadori. *Why Buildings Fall Down.* New York: Norton, 1994.

Lindenthal, Gustav. *Transactions of the American Society of Civil Engineers.* "The Continuous Truss Bridge Over the Ohio River at Sciotoville, Ohio of the Chesapeake and Ohio Northern Railway." Presented 5 April 1922. Vol. LXXXV, Paper No. 1496, American Society of Civil Engineers, 1922.

Lockley, Fred. *History of the Columbia River Valley, From the Dalles to the Sea,* "History of Charles F. Swigert." Chicago: S. J. Clarke, 1928.

Maben, Manley. *Vanport.* Portland, Oregon: Oregon Historical Society Press, 1987.

MacColl, E. Kimbark. *The Growth of a City: Power and Politics in Portland, Oregon 1915-1950.* Portland, Oregon: Georgian Press, 1979.

————. *The Shaping of a City: Business and Politics in Portland, Oregon 1885-1915.* Portland, Oregon: Georgian Press, 1976.

———— with Harry H. Stein. *Merchants, Money, and Power.* Portland, Oregon: Georgian Press, 1988.

Manual of Steel Construction, 6th ed. New York: American Institute of Steel Construction, 1963.

McArthur, Lewis A. and Lewis L. McArthur. *Oregon Geographic Names,* 7th edition. Portland: Oregon Historical Society Press, 2003.

McCullough, Conde B. and Edward S. Thayer. *Elastic Arch Bridges.* New York: John Wiley & Sons, 1931.

McCullough, David. *The Great Bridge.* New York: Simon and Schuster, 1972.

Middleton, William D. *The Bridge at Québec.* Bloomington, Indiana: Indiana University Press, 2001.

Misa, Thomas J. *A Nation of Steel, the Making of Modern America 1865-1925.* Baltimore and London: Johns Hopkins University Press, 1995.

Mock, Elizabeth. *The Architecture of Bridges.* New York: The Museum of Modern Art, 1949.

Morrison, Dorothy. *Outpost: John McLoughlin and the Far West.* Portland: Oregon Historical Society Press, 1999.

Norman, James B. *Portland's Architectural Heritage,* 2nd edition revised. Portland: Oregon Historical Society Press, 1991.

O'Donnell, Terence and Thomas Vaughan. *Portland: An Informal History and Guide.* Portland: Oregon Historical Society Press, 1984.

Orr, Elizabeth L. and William N. *Geology of the Pacific Northwest.* New York: McGraw, 1996.

Pearce, Martin and Richard Jobson. *Bridge Builders.* Chichester, England: Wiley-Academy, 2002. On pp. 92-109, see bridges designed by Jiri Strasky, co-designer of arch bridge on Springwater Trail over McLoughlin Boulevard in Portland.

Petroski, Henry. *Engineers of Dreams: Great Bridges and the Spanning of America.* New York: Knopf, 1995.

————. *To Engineer Is Human, the Role of Failure in Successful Design.* New York: Vintage, 1992.

————. *Pushing the Limits: New Adventures in Engineering.* New York: Vintage, 2005. See discussion of Portland's bridges in chapter on "Bridges of America," pp. 13-20.

Piper, Linda J., ed. *The Millennium Bridge Crossing the Kennebec River.* Maine: Sagadahoc Bridge Dedication Committee, 2000.

Plowden, David. *Bridges: The Spans of North America.* New York: Norton, 1974.

Price, Larry W., ed. *Portland's Changing Landscape.* Portland, Oregon: Geography Department, Portland State University–Association of American Geographers, 1987.

Rastorfer, Darl. *Six Bridges, the Legacy of Othmar H. Ammann.* New Haven: Yale University Press, 2000. Describes Ammann's involvement with Gustav Lindenthal's 1920s Portland bridges.

Reier, Sharon. *The Bridges of New York.* Mineola, New York: Dover, 2000.

Salvadori, Mario. *The Art of Construction, Projects and Principles for Beginners.* Chicago: Chicago Review Press, 1990.

————. *Why Buildings Stand Up.* New York: W.W. Norton, 1980.

Scott, Harvey W. *History of the Oregon Country.* Cambridge: Riverside Press, 1924.

Scott, Richard. *In the Wake of Tacoma: Suspension Bridges and the Quest for Aerodynamic Stability.* Reston, Virginia: American Society of Civil Engineers, 2001.

Smith, Dwight, James Norman and Pieter Dykman. *Historic Highway Bridges of Oregon,* 2nd edition revised. Portland: Oregon Historical Society Press, 1989.

Snyder, Eugene E. *Early Portland: Stump-Town Triumphant.* Portland: Binford and Mort, 1979.

————. Portland *Names and Neighborhoods.* Portland: Binford and Mort, 1979.

State of Oregon, Office of the Oregon Secretary of State. *Oregon Blue Book 2005-2006.* Salem: 2005.

Steinman, David B. *The Builders of the Bridge: The Story of John Roebling and His Son.* New York: Harcourt, Brace and Company, 1945.

———— and Sara Ruth Watson. *Bridges and Their Builders.* 2nd edition revised. New York: Dover, 1941.

———— and John T. Nevill. *Miracle Bridge at Mackinac.* Grand Rapids, Michigan: Wm. B. Eerdmans, 1957.

Structural Steel Detailing. Chicago: American Institute of Steel Construction, 1981.

Talese, Gay. *The Bridge.* New York: Harper and Row, 1964.

The American Cable Company. *The World's Greatest Suspension Bridge: Philadelphia to Camden.* New York: The American Cable Company, Inc., 1926.

Waddell, J.A.L. *Bridge Engineering.* 2 vols. New York: John Wiley & Sons, 1916.

————. *De Pontibus, a Pocket-Book for Bridge Engineers,* revised. New York: John Wiley & Sons, 1906.

————. *Proceedings of the Second Pan American Scientific Congress, Section V, Engineering.* Vol. VI, "Vertical Lift Bridges." Washington, D.C.: GPO, 1917.

Watson, Wilbur J. *Bridge Architecture.* New York: William Helburn, 1927.

———— and Sara Ruth Watson. *Bridges in History and Legend.* Introduction by William E. Wickenden. Cleveland, Ohio: J.H. Jansen, 1937.

Wilson, Forrest. *Bridges Go From Here to There.* Washington, D.C.: Preservation Press, 1993.

Wood, Sharon M. (text)*The Portland Bridge Book.* Portland: Oregon Historical Society Press, 1989.

Wood Wortman, Sharon M. (text) *The Portland Bridge Book,* 2nd edition revised and expanded. Portland: Oregon Historical Society Press, 2001.

Yi-sheng, Mao. *Bridges in China, Old and New.* Peking: Foreign Language Press, 1978.

PERIODICALS

"Advancing into a New Generation," *Engineering News Record*, 2 April 1981. Article on Glenn L. Jackson Bridge.

"Al Monner Looks Back at the 45-Year History of the St. Johns Bridge," *Oregon People,* Jan.-Feb. 1976.

"Better Roads 1999 Bridge Inventory," *Better Roads,* Nov. 1999.

"A Bridge at Sellwood," *Oregon Voter Digest,* 16 Sept. 1922.

Buckley, Tom. "A Reporter at Large (The Hell Gate Bridge)," *The New Yorker,* 14 Jan. 1991, pp. 37-59.

"Columbia Crossing? A Big Hit!" *News,* Oregon Department of Transportation, June 1983.

"Construction in the West 50 Years Ago, the Bridges of Portland," *Western Construction,* Jan. 1975, p. 49.

"Council Gives Green Light to Stadium Freeway," *The Oregonian,* 23 March 1962, p. 1.

"County Wins," *County Lines,* Oct. 1979.

Cunningham, R.O., H. Erzurumlu, and R.A. Leber. "Construction of the Fremont Bridge," American Society of Civil Engineers Meeting Preprint No. 1968, ASCE National Structural Engineering Meeting, San Francisco, April 1973.

Domreis, Oliver J. "Multnomah County Bridges," *County Engineer,* 27 Aug. 1977.

"Engineer License Law Being Enforced in Oregon," *Engineering News-Record,* Vol. 96, 1 Jan.-30 June 1926, p. 254.

Green, Peter. "Contractor Bridges Gap in a Hectic 72 Hours," *Engineering News-Record,* 7 Sept. 1989. Describes replacement of swing span with vertical lift span at BNSF Railway Bridge 5.1.

Harwood, Allan C. "I-205 Columbia River Bridge—Design and Construction Highlights." *Prestressed Concrete Institute Journal*, Vol. 27, No. 2, March April 1982.

Hedefine, Alfred and Louis G. Silano. "Design of the Fremont Bridge," American Society of Civil Engineers Meeting Preprint No. 1210, April 1970.

Hill, Richard L. and Noelle Crombie. "Finding Fault Adds to Earthquake Risk," *The Oregonian,* 30 May 2001, A1.

Howard, E.E. "Interstate Bridge over the Columbia River, Portland, Ore.," *Engineering News,* Vol. 73, No. 25, 21 June 1915.

Koiv, Vello and Bernard Hopfinger. "Fast Track, Instant Track," *Civil Engineering,* Oct. 1989. Describes replacement of swing span with vertical lift span at BNSF Railway Bridge 5.1.

Learn, Scott and Angie Chuang. "Limits Put on Sellwood Bridge," *The Oregonian,* 23 June 2004.

Merchant, Ivan D. "Construction of the Columbia River (Portland-Vancouver) Bridges," *Journal of the Construction Division,* American Society of Civil Engineers, Sept. 1959.

"Motor Vehicles per Driving Age Population in 2004," *State Rankings 2006* (Kansas: Morgan Quitno Press), p. 558.

Moyano, Dave. "Historic Preservation," *Bridges,* Jan.-Feb. 2006, p. 30. Describes rehabilitation of Broadway Bridge.

"New Route Cuts Swatch Through Old Portland," *The Oregonian,* 3 Feb. 1964, p. 5.

"1999 Fremont Bridge Peregrine Falcon Update," *Audubon Warbler,* Aug. 1999, p. 9.

Polhemus, James H. "Building an Airport at Portland, Oregon." *Engineering News-Record,* Vol. 100, 1 Jan-30 June 1928, pp. 928-930.

"Progress to be Noted, Waterfront Project to be Dedicated Today," *The Oregonian,* 7 June 1929, p. 12.

"Statement by Tom Edwards, State Highway Engineer, Concerning the Cracked Girder in the Fremont Bridge," News Release 72-71-S, Oregon State Highway Division Public Information Office, 21 March 1972.

Shedd, Jack P. "Burlington Northern Railroad Swing Span Replacement." Paper presented to Northwest Bridge Engineering Seminar, Portland, Ore., 8 Oct. 1985.

Steinman, D.B. "The St. Johns Bridge at Portland, Oregon," *Military Engineers,* July-Aug. 1933.

Stewart, Bill. "City of Bridges," *The Oregonian,* 27 Aug. 1997, A19.

————. "Diagnosis of Trunnion Crack Requires Series of High-Tech Tests," *The Oregonian,* 27 Aug. 1997, A19.

Svenson, George. "Oregon Bridge Features Innovative Bell Piers, Floating Falsework." *Civil Engineering* , April 1981. Article on Glenn L. Jackson Bridge.

Tokola, Alpo and Edward J. Wortman. "Erecting the Center Span of the Fremont Bridge," *Civil Engineering,* July 1973.

Touran, Ali and Alex Okereke. "Performance of Orthotropic Bridge Decks," *Journal of Performance of Constructed Facilities,* American Society of Civil Engineers, Vol. 5, No. 2, May 1991.

"TY Lin Celebrates Chongquing's Record-Breaking Duo," *Bridge Design & Engineering,* 1 Sept. 2004. Describes design of Caiyuanba Yangtze River Bridge, with world's longest tied arch span.

Wood, Sharon M. "Willamette's Bridges—their History Spans Decades," *The Oregonian*, a continuing series, 25 March-21 May 1984.

Wood, Sharon M. "A Lift to the Future," *Portside,* Jan.-Feb. 1986. Describes plans for replacing swing span with vertical lift span at BNSF Bridge 5.1.

OTHER DOCUMENTS AND SOURCES

California Department of Motor Vehicles. "Statistics for Publication," Policy/Technical Section, Sacramento, 15 July 1998.

California Department of Transportation (Caltrans). "Seismic Retrofit Program," Caltrans Website, Sacramento, 2003.

CBA Engineering and Buckland & Taylor Engineering. "Port Mann Bridge," Vancouver, B.C., 1964.

City of Portland, Department of Public Works. "Traffic Summary for Willamette River Bridges, City of Portland," 18 Nov. 1914.

————, Office of Transportation. "Portland Infrastructure Projects Timeline, Jan. 2000-Dec. 2004," Portland, March 2001.

———— and Multnomah County. "Measures of Increasing Bicycle Use," no date.

David Evans and Associates. "Sauvie Island Bridge Tier I Bridge Siting Study," for Multnomah County, 14 June 2002.

Davidson, Hugh. "Sauvie Island Bridge," for Multnomah County, 7 Feb. 2005. Historical report on 1950 bridge.

Ellis, Aaron. "Port of Portland Historical Timelines, 1891-1998," Port of Portland, 1998.

Federal Highway Administration. "Status of the Nation's Highways, Bridges, and Transit: 2002 Conditions and Performance Report," FHWA Website. See Part III Bridges, Chapter 11: "Federal Bridge Program Status of the Nation's Bridges."

Front Street Intercepting Sewer and Drainage System, contract, J.F. Shea Co. and City of Portland, 29 July 1927, Stanley Parr Archives, City of Portland.

Hargreaves Associates, et al. "Eastbank Riverfront Park Master Plan," for the City of Portland, Jan. 1994.

Harrington, John Lyle and Ernest E. Howard. "Final Report. The Columbia River Interstate Bridge," for Multnomah County, Oregon and Clark County, Washington, 1918.

Hirota, Mark, Oregon State Bridge Engineer, to Christie Holmgren, Sr. Community Affairs Coordinator, Region 1 Community Affairs. "Bridge Condition," news release from Oregon Department of Transportation, Salem, 10 May 2000.

Historic American Engineering Record (HAER), National Park Service, U.S. Department of the Interior. Prints and Photographs Division, Library of Congress:

Dodds, Linda. "St. Johns Bridge," OR-40, Addendum (draft cover page), 2001.

————. "Marquam Bridge," OR-106 (draft cover page), 2001.

Grzowski, Kenneth J. "Willamette River Bridge" (Oregon City). OR-31, 1990.

Link, Gary. "Broadway Bridge," OR-22, 1990.

————. "Hawthorne Bridge," OR-20, 1990.

————. "Steel Bridge," OR-21, 1990.

————. "St. Johns Bridge," OR-40, 1990.

McGaw, Judith. "Broadway Bridge," OR-22, Addendum (draft), 2001.

————. "Hawthorne Bridge," OR-20, Addendum (draft), 2001.

————. "Morrison Bridge," OR-100 (draft), 2001.

————. "Steel Bridge," OR-21, Addendum (draft), 2001.

Staehli, Alfred. "Willamette 5.1," OR-26, Port-8, 1985.

Wood Wortman, Sharon. "Burnside Bridge," OR-101 (draft), 2001.

————. "Fremont Bridge," OR-104 (draft), 2001.

————. "Ross Island Bridge," OR-102 (draft), 2001.

————. "Sellwood Bridge," OR-103 (draft), 2001.

Laurgaard, Olaf. "Treatise on the Design, Test and Construction of the Front St. Intercepting Sewer and Drainage System in Portland, Oregon, including Intercepting Sewer, Pumping Plant and Concrete Bulkhead-Wall on Gravel Filled Timber Cribs," written for the American Society of Civil Engineers, pp. 1-81. Stanley Parr Archives, uncatalogued, City of Portland.

Lawrence, Holford and Allyn (Sydney B. Hayslip, Supervising Architect). "Park It and Market," *The Architectural Forum*, Oct. 1934.

Modjeski, Ralph. "The Vancouver-Portland Bridges: A Report to Mr. Howard Elliot, President of the Northern Pacific Railroad Co. and to Mr. John F. Stevens, President of the Spokane, Portland & Seattle Railway Co.," Chicago, 1910.

Multnomah County Commissioners' Bridge Journals, 11 volumes. Multnomah County Yeon Records Center: "Burnside and Ross Island Bridges," Vol. 1, 9 Aug. 1922 to 29 Dec. 1924, pp. 1-400.

————, Vol. 2, 29 Dec. 1924 to 12 Dec. 1927, pp. 1-376.

"Ross Island and Sellwood Bridges," 25 April 1923 to 1 Aug. 1927, pp. 1-192.

"Broadway Bridge Reconstruction and Lovejoy Ramp," 19 April 1926 to 5 Nov. 1928, pp. 1-140.

"Columbia River Interstate Bridge Commission," Vol. 1, 29 Nov. 1913 to 10 Feb. 1920, pp. 1-295.

————, Vol. 2, 9 March 1920 to 14 Oct. 1924, pp. 1-300.

————, Vol. 3, 14 Oct. 1924 to 8 June 1944, pp. 1-438.

"St. Johns Bridge," Vol. 1, 31 Jan. 1928 to 27 Dec. 1930, pp. 1-398.

————, Vol. 2, 29 Oct. 1930 to 25 Oct. 1932, pp. 1-191.

"Morrison Street Bridge and Hawthorne Bridge Approach," 24 Nov. 1953 to 13 Sept. 1956, pp. 1-350. "Hawthorne Bridge Approaches," 13 Sept. 1956 to 30 April 1959, pp. 1-228.

"National Directory, Heavy Movable Structures Industry," Bridge Edition. Tallahassee, Florida: Doherty & Associates, 1994.

Newell, J.N. "Future Bridges Over Portland Harbor." Letter to Dr. Gustav Lindenthal, 14 Dec. 1925. Multnomah County Central Library.

————. "Report on Type and Location of Proposed New Bridge at Morrison Street," to the City Planning Commission, Portland, June 1927. Multnomah County Yeon Records Center.

Oregon Department of Transportation (ODOT). "A Chronological History of the Oregon Department of Transportation, 1899 to August 1993," Salem, Ore., Aug. 1993.

————. "Engineering Antiquities Inventory" Historic Bridge Survey Schedule: Broadway, Burnside, Hawthorne, Ross Island, St. Johns, and Sellwood bridges, Salem, Ore., April 1981, Form EAI-1.

————. "Stadium Freeway, I-405," brochure about the Fremont Bridge, Salem, Ore., 1973.

————. "Glenn L. Jackson Memorial Bridge (Columbia River I-205)," Salem, Ore., no date.

Oregon Department of Geology and Mineral Industries. "Earthquake scenario and probabilistic ground shaking maps for the Portland, Oregon metropolitan area," IMS-15 and IMS-16, 2000.

————. "Oregon Geology," Vol. 60. No. 6, November/December 1998.

"Oregon's Covered Bridges," brochure by the Albany Visitors Association, Albany, Oregon, ca. 2000.

Patrick, Kenneth G. "Gustav Lindenthal: Premier Bridge Designer of the Age of Iron," research paper, Dept of Civil Engineering, Princeton, 1990.

"Portland Harbor Wall," Eastbank Esplanade urban marker and interpretive panel, 2001.

Ranta, Derek. "History of Portland Willamette River Bridges," Capitol Hill School 5th Grade Think Shop Project, May 1983.

"Registered Professional Engineer No. 1, Oregon, Nov. 8, 1919, O. Laurgaard," stamp imprint signed "O Laurgaard," engineering drawing, City of Portland Department of Transportation, Bridge Section.

Ross De Alessi Lighting Design. "City of Bridges: A Master Plan for Lighting the Bridges in Cleveland's Flats," for the Cleveland Bicentennial Commission, no date.

Sverdrup & Parcel, Inc. and Moffatt, Nichol & Taylor. "Morrison Bridge, Multnomah County Oregon." Final Construction Report. Portland: 1958. Multnomah County Yeon Records Center.

Tang, Man-Chung and John Sun. "Design of the Main Spans of the Chongqing, China, Caiyuanba Bridge," Boston: 6th International Bridge Engineering Conference, 2005. Describes design of world's longest tied arch bridge span.

U.S. Army Corps of Engineers. "Bridges Over the Navigable Waters of the United States," Part 4, Pacific Coast. USGPO: Washington, D.C., 1961.

U.S. Department of the Interior, National Park Service, Historic American Engineering Record (HAER), Prints and Photographs Division, Library of Congress, Washington, DC.

U.S. Department of the Interior, National Park Service, National Register of Historic Places. Registration for Willamette River (Oregon City) Bridge (No. 357), 17 May 2005.

Wintermute, Marjorie. "Architecture as a Basic Curriculum Builder," 2nd edition revised. Portland, Oregon: Regional Arts and Culture Council, Architects in Schools Program, 1999.

RESEARCH FILES

Bicycle Transportation Alliance, Portland

Carol Mayer-Reed Landscape Architects, Portland

William Choate, Castro Valley, California

Civil engineering firms (U.S. and Canada)

Clackamas County Historical Society, Oregon City, Oregon

The Dalles Historical Society, The Dalles, Oregon

Steven Dotterrer, Portland

Engineering News-Record (ENR)

Federal Highway Administration, Salem, Oregon and Washington, D.C.

Housing Authority of Portland, Portland

Rodney Keyser, Portland

Lone Fir Cemetery, Portland

Louis Dreyfus Co., Portland

Metro Pioneer Cemeteries, Portland

Metro Regional Government, Data Resource Center and Cemeteries, Portland

Morse Brothers, Clackamas

Multnomah County Library Reference Line, Portland

Multnomah County Transportation Division, Bridge Section and Yeon Records Center

Oregon Department of Transportation, Bridge Engineering, Salem and Portland; Maintenance, Clackamas and Milwaukie; Archives, Salem

Oregon Historical Society, Portland

Oregon Maritime Museum, Portland

Oregon State Library, Salem

Oregon State Historic Preservation Office, Salem

The Oregonian Publishing Co., Portland, especially the columns, "Portland of Years Past," by June Boone

Pioneer-Columbian Cemetery, Portland

Port of Portland, Portland

City of Portland: Bureau of Environmental Services, Portland Development Commission, Stanley Parr Archives and Record Center, Transportation and Engineering (Bridges)

Portland State University Center for Population Research, Portland

River View Cemetery, Portland

San Juan Cemetery, San Juan County, California

Alpo Tokola, Tokola Corp., Portland

Union Pacific Railroad, Portland

WEB PAGES

The following Web addresses were accurate and accessible at the time of publication:

California Department of Transportation (Caltrans), Seismic Retrofit Program for Bridges
<www.dot.ca.gov/hq/paffairs/about/retrofit.htm>

City of Portland, Portland Streetcar
<www.portlandstreetcar.org>

City of Portland, Bureau of Planning, Historic Preservation
<www.portlandonline.com/planning>

City of Portland, Office of Transportation, Transportation Timeline
<www.portlandonline.com/transportation>

City of Portland, Portland Parks & Recreation
<www.portlandonline.com/parks>

Federal Highway Administration
<www.fhwa.dot.gov>

Multnomah County, Dept. of Community Services, Transportation Division, Bridge Section
<www.co.multnomah.or.us/bridge/index.html>

NOVA Superbridge
<www.pbs.org/wgbh/nova/bridge>

Oregon Historical Society
<www.ohs.org>

Port of Portland, About the Port
<www.portofportland.com/>

State of Oregon, Department of Environmental Quality (DEQ), Portland
<www.deq.state.or.us>

State of Oregon, Department of Transportation (ODOT), Bridge Engineering
<www.oregon.gov/ODOT/HWY/BRIDGE>

State of Oregon, Department of Transportation (ODOT), Geo-Environmental Section, Historic Bridges, Portland
<www.oregon.gov/ODOT/HWY/GEOENVIRONMENTAL/historic_bridges_Portland1.shtml>

State of Oregon, Department of Transportation (ODOT), Historic Columbia River Highway
<www.oregon.gov/ODOT/HWY/HCRH>

State of Oregon, Department of Transportation (ODOT), Transportation Management Operations Center
<www.tripcheck.com>

TriMet, A History of Public Transit in Portland
<www.trimet.org/about/history/transitinportland.htm>

US. Environmental Protection Agency
<www.epa.gov>

U.S. Environmental Protection Agency, Region 10 Pacific Northwest, Oregon Superfund Sites
<www.epa.gv/r10earth>

U.S. Department of the Interior, National Park Service, Historic American Building Survey/Historic American Engineering Record, Collections
<www.cr.nps.gov/habshaer/>

Willamette Light Brigade
<www.lightthebridges.org>

Willamette Shore Trolley
<www.oregonelectricrailway.org>

Willamette Valley Covered Bridges
<www.gorp.com/gorp/activity/byway/or_willa.htm>

Also see web pages listed in chapter on Bridge Owners and Other Bridge Resources.

ACKNOWLEDGMENTS

To the Oregon Historical Society Press, for publishing the first two editions of this book, and to Jay Dee Alley, for his drawings, and Bruce Taylor Hamilton and Adair Law, our editors. Without the first and second editions, there could be no third.

To Diane Lund and Derek Ranta. Diane's story, "Study Makes Boy Expert on City's Bridges" (*The Oregonian*, 10 June 1983), led me to Derek, a fifth grader who had compiled a list of the bridges' names, types, construction dates, costs, span lengths, number of lanes, feet above water, and owners—Derek's "Portland Bridge Data Sheet" was the first place from which I could begin to arrange my own understanding.

To Nancy Harger at Portland Parks & Outdoor Recreation, for sponsoring walks for the public and to all the students and their teachers and parents who know these bridges as homework.

To Multnomah County, especially Stan Ghezzi, Tony Lester, Fayez Hjouj, and Dennis Dexter, for making it possible for curious taxpayers to go inside the bascule pit and tower of the Morrison Bridge. Also to Ian Cannon, for his contributions to the chapter How and Why Bridges Are Built.

To former Oregon Department of Transportation historian and now friend Dwight Smith who, during my first research trips to Salem, opened up his files, and said, "Take all the time you need."

To Geoff Bowyer, Karla Keller, Leann Linson, Jack Wood, and others at ODOT, for allowing my ongoing research in their Transportation Management Operations Center and other rooms of Region One. To ODOT's Robert Hadlow, Robert Schmidt, Bruce Johnson, and Frank Nelson for always returning my e-mails and phone calls.

To Craig Totten of KPFF Engineering, for help clarifying seismic design, and to Donna Matrazzo, for Sauvie Island facts. In fact, to all the citizens, bridge operators, mechanics, electricians, maintenance workers, traffic analysts (bicycle, pedestrian, and vehicle), graphic artists, public relations staff, writers, statisticians, planners, historians, and engineers (you know who you are), for keeping me informed about changing bridge conditions.

To John DeLacy, for his explanation that anyone can build a bridge so it will stand up, but it takes an engineer to design a bridge so it will barely stand up, another way of saying efficiency with materials comes first in public works construction.

Fremont Bridge.

To Eric DeLony, for hiring me in 1999 to help document the lower Willamette River bridges for the Historic American Engineering Record/ National Park Service, research that led to my understanding each bridge's contribution to the greater history of engineering.

To HAER/NPS for use of photographs taken by James Norman during the 1999 Willamette River Bridges (WRB) Recording Project, many of them included in this book, and to ODOT, Multnomah County, the Oregon Historical Society, Hugh Ackroyd, Steve Dotterer, David Evans & Associates, Frank Engel, Mark Falby, Linda Hardin, Jay Murphy, James Norman, and Bob Sallinger and the Audubon Society of Portland for use of drawings and/or historic and contemporary photographs.

To HAER/NPS for use of "Common Historic Truss Designs," and the measured drawings created during the WRB study.

To James Norman, for producing this book and keeping us on schedule, and to Mark Falby, for his design and layout—days spent kerning, cutting, pasting, adjusting, and resizing.

To Bruce Douglas from Citizens Photo in Portland, for overnight rendering of slides and historic photographs into tifs and jpegs. To Lucy Berkley (Kopp) at the Oregon Historical Society, for her unbureaucratic assistance.

To Charlie White, for his command of OED English; to Michael McDowell, for help finding what we needed in *The Chicago Manual of Style*; to Brian Doyle, for his suggestions; and to the skilled Amy Platt, for her double-quick indexing.

To Christine Rains, for creating and updating the "Portland Bridges Map," and to graphic artist Josh Axtell, for his design of the Urban Adventure logo, introduced with this book.

To the City of Portland Office of Transportation, for use of "Portland Transportation History Timeline," and to TriMet, for use of "A History of Public Transit in Portland."

To Stephen Cohen, for his song "Bridges of This Town."

To Nathan Baptiste, for his poem "The Sellwood Bridge."

To Ralph Nelson, for his song "The Bridges In Town Go Up and Down."

To Amira Shagaga, for her poem "Rough Steel."

To *Windfall—A Journal of Poetry of Place*, for permission to reprint "Bridges that Open Like Oysters."

To Al Tokola, president of the engineering firm of the same name, who, in 1972, researched the cause of the Fremont Bridge's fracture, and then not only answered all my questions 21 years later about what had gone wrong, but also introduced me to his extraordinary partner.

To Ed Wortman, my primary proofreader and expert in engineering-ese, for making possible the scope of this third edition.

To Portland, a city I love like it's a family, and to my family, from here to Moosehead Lake, Maine.

ILLUSTRATION SOURCES

All images are copyrighted by the photographers and illustrators and in some instances by the lender/lending institution.

t = top, l = left, tl = top left, tr = top right, c = center, cl = center left, cr = center right, b = bottom, br = bottom right

Hugh Ackroyd, Ackroyd Photography, Inc.: 25r, 26l/r;

Joseph Boquiren: 4, 149-154;

Steve Dotterrer collection: ix, 46t, 54b, 84l/r, 181, 197t;

David Evans & Associates: 127;

Frank Engel: 40b, 42;

Mark Falby and Mark Falby collection: frontispiece, 2, 16, 17l/r, 20l/r, 33, 40t, 49l/r, 70, 72, 76, 97t/b, 108, 110l, 119, 120t/b, 125, 132, 181, 197b, 200, 208, colophon;

Linda Hardin: 182;

Historic American Engineering Record/National Park Service (HAER/NPS): 135-148, 156, 207;

HAER/NPS by James Norman: xiii, 8, 9, 11, 15, 21, 23, 24, 28r, 29, 31, 32, 36, 37, 39, 41, 43, 45, 46b, 50, 51, 53, 56r-59, 61, 64tr/b-67, 69, 71, 73-75, 77, 78, 81, 83, 85l/r, 86-88, 95, 96, 98, 99, 199;

HAER/NPS by James Norman, enhanced by Mark Falby: 18, 159, 160, 165, 171-173, 175, 176;

Multnomah County Bridge Section: 7, 35l/r, 38, 47, 48, 64tl, 79, 82, 102, 130, 131;

Jay Murphy, Murphy Pacific Corp.: 25tl/bl, 155;

James Norman: xi, 1, 13, 34, 63, 89, 91-93, 101, 103-105, 107, 109, 110r, 111, 113, 115, 117, 121-123, 126;

Original west end approach to Ross Island Bridge.

U.S.S. Portland *passing beneath the St. Johns Bridge.*

Glenn Jackson Bridge.

James Norman, enhanced by Mark Falby: 157, 166, 167, 168, 169, 170, 174, 195;

Oregon Department of Transportation, Salem: 27l/r, 28l, 62l, 90, 114t/b, 116, 198;

Oregon Historical Society: 54t (OrHi 98518), 55 (OrHi 101314), 80 (OrHi 101315);

Christine Rains, for Urban Adventure Press: vii;

Bob Sallinger, Audubon Society of Portland: 112;

and Sharon Wood Wortman: 19l/r, 56l, 62r, 118.

ABOUT THE AUTHORS

Sharon Wood Wortman, author of *The Portland Bridge Book* (Oregon Historical Society Press, 1989 and 2001), and *Bridge In A Box—Instructions & Patterns for Making Models of Portland's Truss Spans* (Urban Adventure Press 2005), leads bridge walks using poetry as a compass for hundreds and hundreds of students and adults every year for Portland Parks & Outdoor Recreation, OMSI, Saturday Academy, public and private schools, and other groups. She was one of two full-time historians for the 1999 Historic American Engineering Record/National Park Service (HAER/NPS) recording of the Willamette River bridges for the Library of Congress. She is a recipient of the Frances Shaw Fellowship from the Ragdale Artist Colony and her poems have been published in *Windfall—A Journal of Poetry of Place* and *The Sunday Oregonian*, and by the Oregon Council of Teachers of Education. She is a graduate of Linfield College and earned a Master of Education from the University of Portland in 1998. Her website is <www.bridgestories.com>.

Ed Wortman, a member of the American Society of Civil Engineers since 1959, was named the 2004 Engineer of the Year by the Portland chapter of ASCE for contributions to his profession. He was the engineering advisor for the 1999 HAER/NPS Willamette River Bridges Recording Project. He has worked on Ocean Thermal Energy Conversion projects, offshore oil platforms, buildings, and bridges all over the country. In Portland, he was the field engineer working with the ironworkers to erect the side spans and then the 6,000-ton center span of the Fremont Bridge, and construction engineer for the $38 million reconstruction of BNSF Bridge 5.1 from a swing bridge to a vertical lift. He was the project administrator in charge of Multnomah County's $21.5 million rehabilitation of the Hawthorne Bridge in 1999, and now serves as a member of the team building a new Sauvie Island Bridge. He graduated with a B.A. and Master of City Planning from Harvard, and an M.S. in Civil Engineering from the University of California at Berkeley.

Building of the St. Johns Bridge.

James Norman is the Cultural Resources Manager for the Oregon Department of Transportation. He has documented more than 100 of Oregon's most significant resources for the Historic American Engineering Record (HAER) and Historic American Building Survey (HABS). He was the official photographer for the 1999 HAER/NPS Willamette River Bridges Recording Project. He is also the author, photographer, designer, and producer of *Oregon Main Street: A Rephotographic Survey* (OHS, 1994), and *Portland's Architectural Heritage* (OHS, 1991), and the co-author/principal photographer for *Historic Highway Bridges of Oregon* (OHS, 1989). His documentary photography has been widely published, and is included in several permanent collections, including the collections of the Smithsonian Institution and the Library of Congress. He has a Bachelor of Science in Communications from Louisiana State University.

Joseph Boquiren is an architect with Myhre Group Architects in Portland. He was one of six architects for the 1999 HAER Willamette River Bridges Recording Project and served as the project's field foreman. He won first place in *The Oregonian* newspaper's 2005 Christmas Cartoon Drawing Competition. He graduated with a Master of Architecture from the University of Maryland.

Charlie White, Distinguished (Emeritus) Professor of History, taught at Portland State University 1952-2006. He was the PSU Director of International Education 1970-1985, and Director of Summer Session 1970-1989. He has a B.A. and M.A. from Michigan State College, and a Ph.D. from the University of Southern California.

Mark Falby, a Publication Design Specialist for the Oregon Department of Transportation, provides graphics, illustrations, and layout to ODOT and other state agencies. His work on the *Oregon Bike Plan* won national attention, with his illustrations shared with other publications nationwide. His work on the *Columbia River Gorge Bike Map* won a national publication award. His fine art works are found in many private collections. He graduated with a B.F.A. in Fine Arts from the University of Oregon, and a Master of Art Education from Western Oregon State College.

INDEX

Editor's note: Page numbers in italic refer to illustrations and photographs

BRIDGES OF THIS TOWN

by Stephen Cohen

bridges of this town, bridges of this town
they go up, they go down
bridges of this town, bridges of this town
they help me get around

on foot, in a car, in a truck,
hey, good luck!
in a boat, from a plane, on a train, in the rain
it's just the same
in a bus, on a bike, day and night,
I feel all right, in the sight, of the bridges of this town . . .

I guess the first bridge I came to was the Marquam,
I was passing through on I-5
I enjoyed the view of downtown and the other bridges
and the mountains in the distance

I've walked on the Morrison in the morning sun,
I've jogged on the St. John's in a marathon,
with blisters on my feet, in the noon October heat

I've been on the Hawthorne by mistake,
we had to wait at the crossing gate
while we watched the wake of a passing ship
I've been on the brick red Broadway,

I've followed a Rose Parade on the Burnside
with thousands lined on its sides,
they could tell you quite a tale of the light rail
on the Steel, I feel the river run below
you can feel this city breathe from the bridges of this town

bridges of this town, bridges of this town
they go up, they go down

one day, there may be a catastrophe,
the mountains may erupt,
the earth might open up
the Willamette could catch fire,
these bridges could expire
but let's not think about that now
we'll cross that bridge when we get to it

bridges of this town, bridges of this town
they go up, they go down
bridges of this town, bridges of this town
they help me get around
bridges of this, bridges of this,
bridges of this Portland, Oregon town

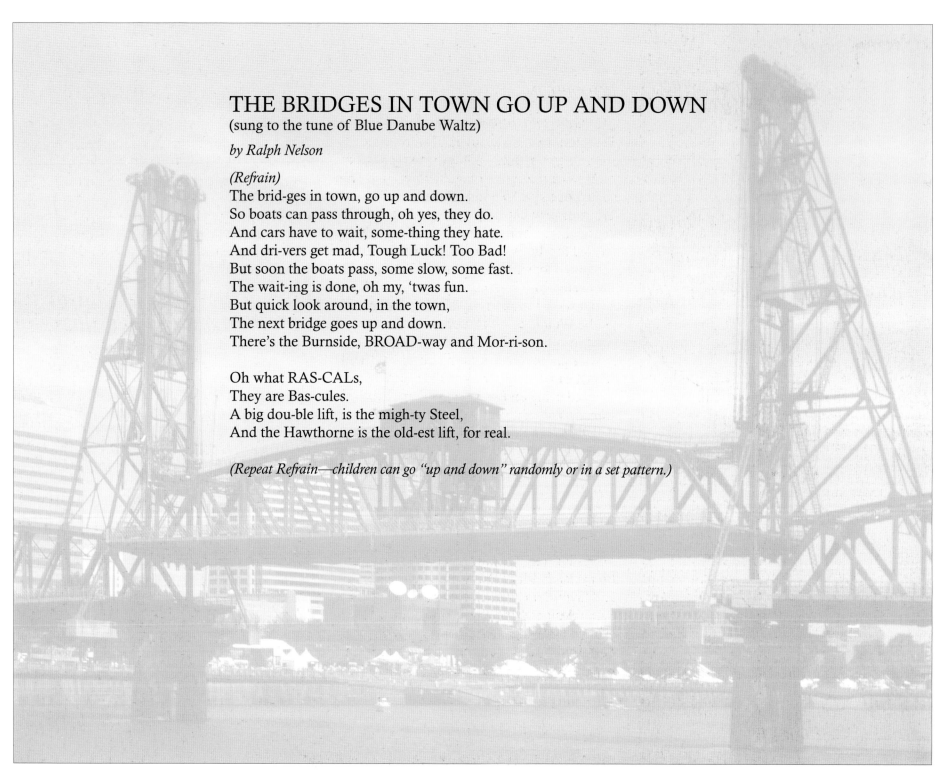

THE BRIDGES IN TOWN GO UP AND DOWN
(sung to the tune of Blue Danube Waltz)

by Ralph Nelson

(Refrain)
The brid-ges in town, go up and down.
So boats can pass through, oh yes, they do.
And cars have to wait, some-thing they hate.
And dri-vers get mad, Tough Luck! Too Bad!
But soon the boats pass, some slow, some fast.
The wait-ing is done, oh my, 'twas fun.
But quick look around, in the town,
The next bridge goes up and down.
There's the Burnside, BROAD-way and Mor-ri-son.

Oh what RAS-CALs,
They are Bas-cules.
A big dou-ble lift, is the migh-ty Steel,
And the Hawthorne is the old-est lift, for real.

(Repeat Refrain—children can go "up and down" randomly or in a set pattern.)

208

COLOPHON

The Portland Bridge Book is printed on 100-pound Pacesetter Matte text stock. The cover incorporates a color-build process black design with process color text highlights printed onto coated one-side 80-pound Pacesetter Dull. Titles, display headings, and main body text are set in 12-point Calisto MT, a Roman font created for the resolution of laser printers and photocopying, designed in 1987 by Ron Carpenter for Monotype Corporation. The layout was created using Adobe InDesign CS2 on the Windows XP platform. The Historic American Engineering Record/National Park Service photographs were made with a Cambo 45 NX camera, and the 4"x5" negatives were scanned using an Epson perfection 3200 flatbed scanner, and edited in Adobe Photoshop CS2. Additional photos were prepared as 30MB, 8-bit TIFF files from a Nikon D200 digital SLR and Nikon 12-24 mm DX. Supplementary digital photos were taken with a 4 megapixel camera. Publication was output to PDF and submitted electronically to printer.

James Norman produced *The Portland Bridge Book*. Mark Falby created the design and layout, and James Norman and Mark Falby designed the cover. The book was printed by Bridgetown Printing Co. in Portland, Oregon, and the signatures were smythe-sewn before binding.

Rose Festival dragon boats beneath the Marquam Bridge.